CW01021010

The NAIL SHAPES *&* STRUCTURE COMPENDIUM

*How to create beautiful nail shapes
on any type of nail*

Ela Loszczyk

The Nail Shapes & Structure Compendium

2015 COPYRIGHT © ELA LOSZCZYK

ALL RIGHTS RESERVED. NO PART OF THIS PUBLICATION MAY BE REPRODUCED, DISTRIBUTED, OR TRANSMITED IN ANY FORM OR BY ANY MEANS, INCLUDING PHOTOCOPYING, RECORDING, OR OTHER ELECTRONIC OR MECHANICAL METHODS, WITHOUT THE PRIOR WRITTEN PERMISSION OF THE PUBLISHER, EXCEPT IN THE CASE OF BRIEF QUOTATIONS EMBODIED IN ARTICLES AND CERTAIN OTHER NON COMMERCIAL USES PERMITED BY COPYRIGHT LAW. FOR PERMISSION REQUESTS, WRITE TO THE PUBLISHER, ADDRESSED "ATTENTION: PERMISSIONS COORDINATOR," AT THE ADDRESS BELOW.

Published by NAIL EXPERTS ACADEMY LTD

info@nailexpertsacademy.com

Dedication

—⟋⟋⟍—

TO YOU –

A perfectionist who, like me, loves nails and everything
about them—

Especially perfect structure and shapes.

With love
Ela Loswig

A Note to You

—⁓⁓—

As a nail tech, educator, competition judge and nail champion, I've been blessed to learn and work with world class educators and artists. Participation in many training courses allowed me to learn bits and pieces from each one of them; creating my own way of doing nails. That includes the nail structure, form and product application, nail prep, filing and finishing procedures etc., and this is what I'll be teaching you in this book—my technique and how I do it.

I've done my best to present you with the most popular and adequate nail shapes. However, some shapes may be different than what you've imagined or been told previously. As I like to say; every educator is unique and have their own style.

Having said that, I want you to sit back and relax while you read and absorb the knowledge in this book, and once you're done, grab your brush and give all these shapes a go.

With love,

Ela

Contents

Acknowledgment

"Surround yourself with people who are only going to lift you higher"

I'd like to thank from the bottom of my heart, very special people who helped me out in creating this book by giving their expertise, time and tones of positive energy.

Magdalena Walczak – my friend and photographer who was there despite everything.

Kirsty Penny, Ula Wojciak, Dorota Skora and Karolina Dudek - my fantastic and patient models! You were tired of sitting for long hours, but even though, it didn't stop you from making us all laugh.

My Mum for being there whenever I needed her.

And finally:

Lukasz Loszczyk – my husband, my partner, my mentor. I admire you and I'm truly grateful for your endless support.

Hi, I'm Ela

—꿈—

I believe that to be happy and successful you should do what you love and always do your best.

Hi, I'm Ela Loszczyk, founder of **Nail Experts Academy** and author of "Win the Nail Game," and the book you are holding in your hands right now.

My goal is to **help nail technicians get the most out of their potential** so they can provide more effective and better service to their customers, as well as upgrade skills and take them to the next level. I also want to inspire others to be successful in the nail industry by sharing my knowledge and expertise via my live, DVD, and on-line training courses, workshops, articles, step by step tutorials and books.

My passion is to teach in a way that is simple to understand and easy to absorb. I want to teach as many people as possible and with that in mind, I've started my online academy—the Nail Experts Academy (www.nailexpertsacademy.com), and writing books so you can "take me home" and learn from me whenever you want.

Even though it may sound pretty impressive, as you can imagine, a success never happens overnight. It definitely didn't happen to me that way; I had to work really hard to fulfil my dreams. Starting small, growing my business, failing here and there and trying new things, I eventually succeeded.. That's how I got to the point where I felt happy and blessed with everything I have and do now. To me, that's the success – doing what I love, so it never feels like work.

After starting in the nail industry in late 2005, I was determined to achieve something great, and within just 3 years I became a multi-competition winner, holding the title of Scottish and UK Nail Champion. Soon after, I was invited to judge nail competitions in the UK. My articles have been published in leading nail industry magazines, such as Scratch, Your Nails, Paznokcie, and Akademia Paznokcia. I'm enormously proud of my two front covers in Scratch and Paznokcie. I also had my five minutes of fame on the STV television show, "The Hour," where I presented nail art to celebrate FIFA World Cup 2010. I'm a winner of Scratch Stars: Gel Tech of the year 2012, and L&P Tech of the year 2013 and 2014.

I now help many students build their skills and prepare them for competitions. Many of them reach podiums at the very beginning of their career. To me, the best feeling ever is when I hear; "thank you, I couldn't have done it without your help."

I hope that through this book I'll become a small part of your success too. *That's my goal here!* I really want you to use this book as a workbook and your guide to become successful. Make notes on it, bend the corners so it will be easier for you to find something, reach for it whenever you feel the need. Don't just read it, study it!

About this book

—⚬—

After my first book, "Win the Nail Game – Competition success made simple," was published; many people started asking for tips and advice to improve their own "salon" skills, especially the nail structure and shape. I'm going to be honest with you—at first I wasn't sure my advice should be a book. I thought about a video training course, which by the way I've created as well, but after giving it a second thought I realized that the book was the best thing to start with. Why? Because it makes sense to have it all in one easy-to-reach place, whenever needed. A book!

I'm sure you've done a lot of training and self-learning to improve your skills, to make sure this square, oval, stiletto shape was as perfect as you could possibly make this structure. You constantly look for advice wherever you can. And you find it, but; other things you may find are more and more confusing, to where at the end of the day you feel like you actually know less than you did before. I know that feeling, as I've been there myself. For instance, at one workshop I'm being told to apply the form like so, when at the next one I'm hearing something completely opposite! Crazy! What's even more frustrating is that no one was able to explain to me *WHY it should be like this and not like that*, in a manner that would appeal to my way of learning – visualising and analysing everything. And of course they were all demonstrating on "easy to do nails" so that when it comes to dealing with a hooked nail type—not many of these rules applied anymore!

If you're like me—analytical mind and structure maniac who constantly strives for perfection—then you're going to love every single page of this book.

I came to a conclusion, that if this book was going to really teach and help you with understanding the WHAT and HOW, then I have to dig deeper into a subject. Showing you how to create an "X" nail shape on a perfect model is not a problem at all, but then in the real world, every day salon work – how many clients with perfect nails do we have? Not many at all. That's why I've chosen to teach you 8 of the most popular nail shapes based on 3 different natural nail types – standard (normal), hooked and bitten. On top of that I'll show you the application of acrylic and gel in a natural and P&W extension, to make sure it covers absolutely everything, giving you more clarity and understanding. Cool? Cool!

I wouldn't be myself if I hadn't started with crucial and essential technical stuff. That's why I called the first Part of this book; "Fail to prepare, prepare to fail." It says it all. Without that knowledge we are unable to get anywhere, so don't skip it, even if you think, "I know that." There's always something new to be learned, no matter how long you've been doing this. So dig in.

Part II covers: Master Techniques and my top tip methods, which I use all the time over and over again. If you're one of those people who does not like routine – I'm telling you that you're going to change your mind after reading this; as routine is nail techs' best friend.

Finally, Part III – 8/3. You'll learn here how to do those 8 most popular shapes based on 3 natural nail types. You'll learn the differences between the form and product application. I also point out all of the adjustments in filing technique, which you must apply for each shape. I've used my own photos and hand painted diagrams to make sure everything is clear and you're getting a better picture.

I left something special at the end to get you really excited and overwhelmed (in a good way), so be sure to read it too.

Without further talking, let's dig deep.

Part I

Fail to prepare
Prepare to fail

Characteristics of the Three Most Common Natural Nail Types

—ᨓ—

Like I've already said, this book is going to teach you, step by step, the procedure of creating perfect structure and various shapes based on the three most common natural nail types:

- Standard

- Hooked

- Bitten

Why these three nail types? Well, as you can imagine there's plenty more than that, however, my experience shows that these are the three most common. I'm not focusing here on the natural nail, free edge shape, or a shape in general (round, inverted triangle, oval etc.). What is important here is the curvature of that nail as seen from the side view. This aspect is particularly important when it comes to form and product application. You'll find out why in a few minutes.

Most of the shapes I'm going to show you are suitable for any nail type and could be done to any length you wish, or rather your client's wish, with one exception; a nail biter.

> # IMPORTANT!
>
> If your client is an extreme nail biter and there's not much nail left, then you shouldn't extend her nail longer than her fingertip! Your role at that moment is to "play a nurse" and create a way for your client's nails to have a chance to grow back to their natural length and shape. Once this stage has been achieved, and only then, you may extend that nail to any length and shape she desires.

Let me first clarify what a standard, hooked, and bitten natural nail means to me, so there won't be any confusion later on and we'll stay on the same page. To give you the best description, I'm using photos of the hands of my real models.

Standard nail

♦ The nail is naturally curved

♦ It's not flat or like a "spoon"

♦ The curvature starts from the cuticle area and runs through the nail, creating a soft arch

- From the apex it grows straight or very gently downwards, but doesn't create a hook

- Free edge can be any shape

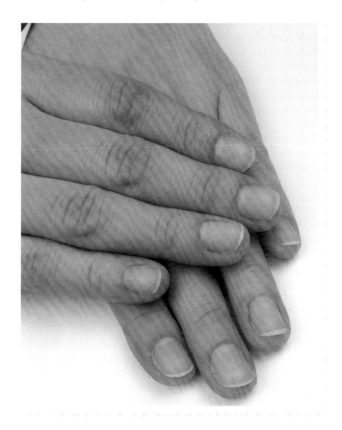

Standard nail type

This type of nail is the easiest to work with, as the form and product application is straight forward and doesn't require a lot of adjustments. If I could choose the type of nails I would like to do every day, no matter when – this would be it.

Hooked nail

- This nail has a dramatic curvature

- From the apex grows downwards creating a "hook" or a "hawk claw"

- Free edge ends in an oval shape mostly

- Hyponychium is high, very often overgrown

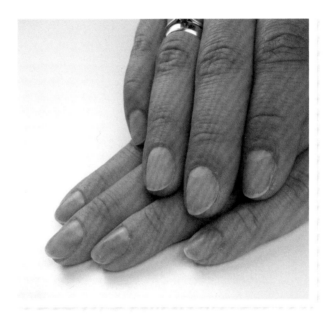

Hooked nail type

To be able to create this desired nail shape, you have to know how to customize and apply the form according to the nail curvature. Once you know the HOW, you won't have any problems with executing the perfect nail structure.

Nail biter

- Short or very short nail plate

- Most of the time flat or very lightly curved

- Free edge (if any) ends in various shapes

- Puffy side walls and fingertips

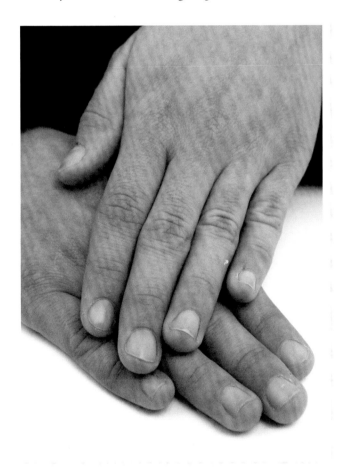

Bitten nail type

This type of nail is very demanding. It requires a lot of precision and form customization, but once you get it right, you're able to achieve   nice results and clients will admire you forever!

NOTE: The model I've used to demonstrate all the shapes is not an excessive nail biter and for that reason, I was able to perform all 8 shapes in a decent length.

Variety of Nail Shapes

Although I've based this book on the eight most popular nail shapes, there are many more than that; and here I will present them to you.

On the diagram below you'll find the majority of nail shapes available today. Why didn't I say *all of them*? By the time I finish writing and you've finished reading this book, it's very likely that a new shape will have been invented. The nail industry evolves at a crazy speed, which I'm sure you've noticed—so saying "all of them" wouldn't be accurate in a very near future.

Several years ago we only knew square and oval plus their similar versions, such as squoval, rounded, almond etc., and that was it. Those main shapes, however, are still extremely popular; having begun all the variations known today.

The diagram below shows you what these shapes look like from the top, side, and front. Those images give you an idea of how the forms must have been applied in order to achieve a specific result – you can see that by the apex placement, free edge shape, and concave. You should study the diagram well and follow these guidelines whenever creating any of these shapes. Keep in mind and consider the type of natural nail you'll be working on; as that may change the form application a little bit.

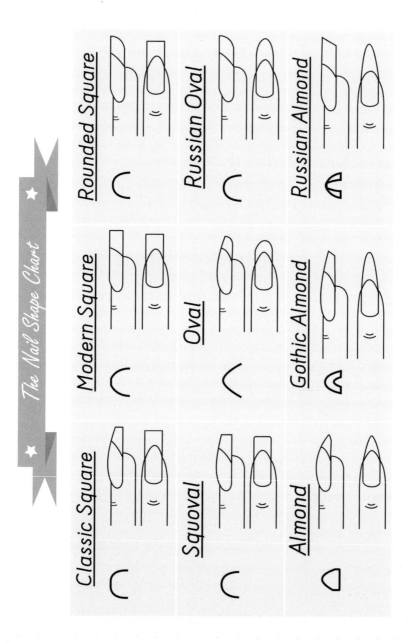

The Nail Shape Chart

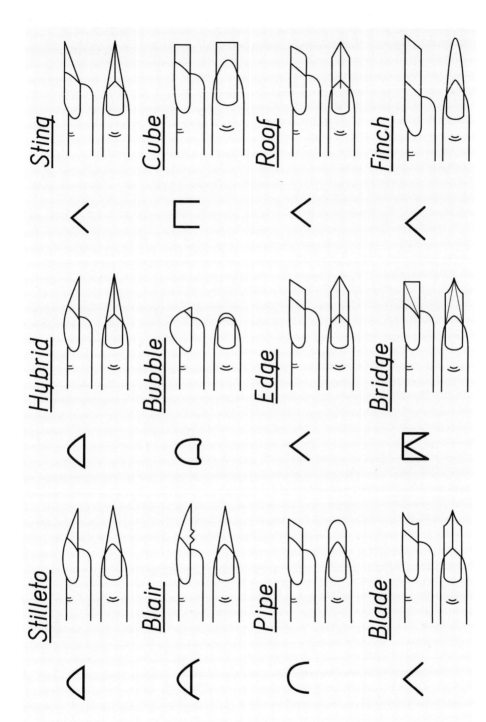

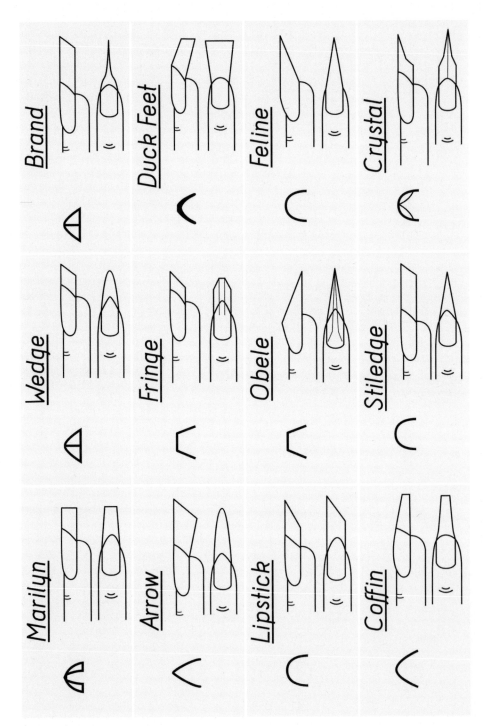

Brand

Duck Feet

Feline

Crystal

Wedge

Fringe

Obele

Stiledge

Marilyn

Arrow

Lipstick

Coffin

How to Determine Best Nail Shape depending on finger length and nail size

When it comes to choosing the right shape for your client, it may be tricky. Unless your client knows exactly what she wants, the decision is on you. You, as a professional, should suggest the best shape to suit her natural nails. The chosen nail shape must elongate and enhance the total appearance of her hand and make your customer feel pretty. You can follow the cuticle shape to establish the free edge shape, but that's not always the case, as sometimes you must consider more aspects, such as finger and nail type, size, and length.

To make it easier for you, I've prepared a diagram that will help to establish the best shape for a specific client, based on her natural nail shape and length of her fingers. This is a very useful tool, so make sure you've got it handy and grab it whenever needed.

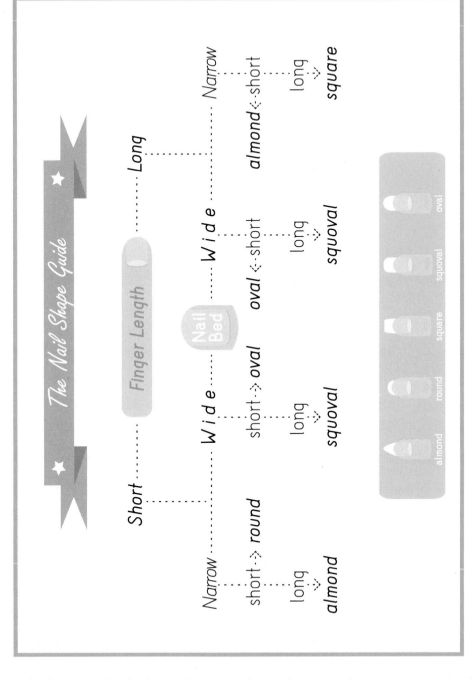

The Nail Shape Guide

Finger Length

Long

Short

Nail Bed

Wide

Wide

Narrow

Narrow

short ⟶ round
long ⟶ almond

short ⟶ oval
long ⟶ squoval

oval ⟵ short
long ⟶ squoval

almond ⟵ short
long ⟶ square

almond | round | square | squoval | oval

Artificial Nail Structure Principles

You may be aware of my online and DVD nail art training courses. I started with them because I love nail art (I even find it kind of therapeutic) and because there was demand. But when it comes to nails, there's something I love even more— a <u>perfectly structured nail</u>—and that, my friend, you should be able to do with your eyes closed, before you start learning anything else.

What do I mean by that? Let me explain it easily by using these two diagrams featuring a square and stiletto shape. These two shapes are fundamental for any other nail shape and you may see the slight difference in their structures. What I'm presenting here is a modern nail structure. It simply means that the apex is always consistent and placed between, or exactly on, 1/3 – 2/3 away from cuticle. From that point the upper arch runs in a straight line to the free edge—square shape, or downwards to the tip of the free edge—almond, stiletto etc.

There's also another method to establish the apex placement, depending on length of the entire extension, and it is called a "cross technique." How it works: – draw a vertical line in the centre of the extended nail (from cuticle to the free edge) and then divide that line in three equal parts. Next draw a horizontal line between the upper two thirds. The junction of those two lines will indicate the stress point and automatically establish the apex.

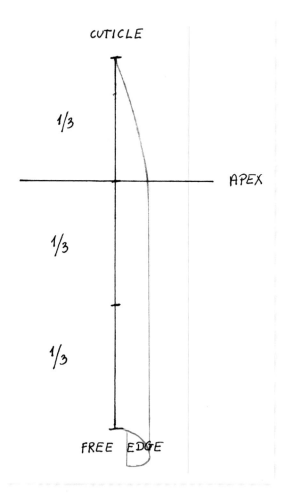

Cross Technique of establishing apex placement

You may have been taught that the nail should create a soft arch and go downwards from the apex, which is also correct and acceptable, but it's an old way and doesn't look as good as the modern one, so I'm not going to spend time on this.

When we're talking about *a nail shape*, in reality we're talking about geometry. It's nothing more than angles, parallel lines, degrees, arches, etc. Every single nail is a mini architectural project, which in order to last long, must be structured well.

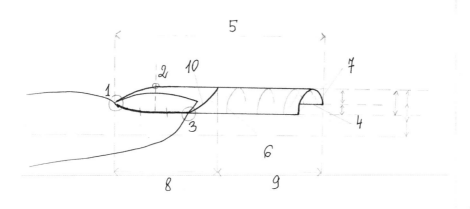

Square nail types

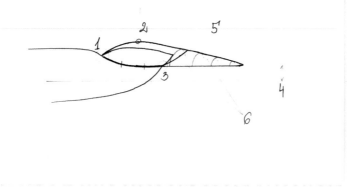

Almond nail types

1 Cuticle area

Product placed here should create a very fine and consistent line, be blended well, and flash to the nail. Make sure you've got a tiny gap, approximately 1 mm between the product and the cuticle to avoid lifting.

2 Apex

The Apex indicates the stress point (the weakest point of the nail) which is the highest point of the nail. Product goes up from the cuticle and from there runs straight to the free edge, or tapers down, such as the case of stiletto, as shown on the picture. I've already explained how to establish its placement, so choose whatever technique you prefer and stick to it; be consistent.

3   Side walls

The Side Walls of the natural nail determine how broad the extended nail should be. The extended free edge should be as narrow as the natural nail is (from side wall to side wall) and consistent in shape through the whole length, in the case of square. The stiletto shape side walls will taper and create a pointy tip.

4   Lower Arch

The Lower arch is determined by the width of the natural side walls and runs consistently. Both sides of the lower arch must be parallel to each other.

5   Upper Arch

The Upper Arch is determined by the Apex. From that point the line tapers down to the cuticle area and runs straight to the extension's free edge in the square shape. In a stiletto, the shape will taper to the free edge as well.

THE SQUARE SHAPE - Lower Arch, Upper Arch and finger's axis line IS PARALLEL!

6 Convex & Concave

The Convex – the exterior curve, and Concave – the interior curve or "the tunnel" are identical and symmetrical through the entire length of the nail. If, for instance, the centre of the nail is thinner than the sides, the nail won't be strong.

7 C-curve & Hair Line

The C-curve depends on the standard – salon and competition. In the salon, that curve will be between 25 – 35% of a circle. The competition standard is 50% of a circle. I'll explain how to pinch the nail in a later chapter. The Hair Line should be a 1-2 tips thick when talking about salon nails, where the competition thickness is no more than a business card.

8 Nail bed elongation

Now days the Nail Bed elongation is so popular that almost every client gets a P&W with the cover pink. When elongating the bed, make sure the colour of the cover pink compliments the customer's skin tone and is in balance with the extension's free edge. By using a mixture of blush and cover pink around the cuticle, you'll get a nice transition from the cover pink to the natural nail.

9 Extension's Free Edge

The Free Edge is as narrow as the natural nail and runs consistently with the side lines. The length of extension's free edge salon standard is determined by several aspects:

- If the nail breaks at the stress point repeatedly, it means that this particular extension is too long. You should keep it shorter or strengthen the stress point.

- If the nail bed is short, you shouldn't create a long extension. The shorter the nail bed – the shorter the extension. If a natural nail is a decent length then you can extend it to any desired and manageable length.

- The safest length of the extension is when it's no longer than the nail bed. If creating longer extensions make sure to build strong enough apex.

10 Smile Line

The easiest way to establish the Smile Line is to recreate the natural nail's free edge. However, when the nail bed is elongated, that rule doesn't apply. For the square shape you may do a soft or deep smile line, and both will look good. For stiletto, almond, and any other pointy shape – create deep lines to complement the final look.

If you find it difficult to establish nice smile lines, follow a Triangle Method. The points where the natural nail detaches from the Hyponychium and its lowest point, create a triangle which forms the structure of your smile line. It's essential that while prepping the nail, you file the free edge very short and to the deepest points/ corners of Hyponychium. Also make sure the points are symmetrically placed.

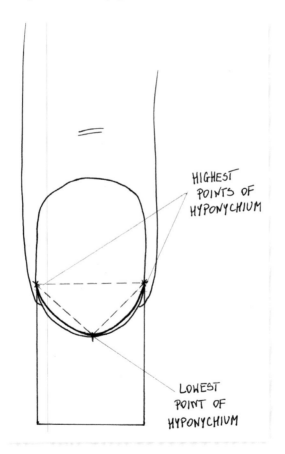

HIGHEST POINTS OF HYPONYCHIUM

LOWEST POINT OF HYPONYCHIUM

Triangle Method of establishing smile line

There you have it. That's the structure I'll be teaching you here. The aim of every single nail technician should be to create that specific shape no matter what natural nail type we work on. The nail on a nail biter should be structured to look exactly the same as the nail done on a hooked or standard type, or any other type. Once you know and understand how to structure the nail then everything comes down to the form application, but that in a moment, first we have more important aspects to talk about. Are you excited? I am!

NOTES:

_____

_____

_____

_____

_____

_____

_____

_____

_____

Part II

MASTER TECHNIQUES

Nail Prep

The correct nail prep is extremely important. There's no doubt about it and I'm sure you agree. It has as much as 70% success when it comes to product adhesion, so if you want to eliminate or minimalize lifting, make sure you do it right and properly.

While doing the prep it's not about removing as many layers of the nail plate as possible, but removing as little as 3 – 5 layers. That's it! You just etch the nail lightly so the product can adhere better to the rugged surface. You can compare that to painting a wooden door for example. Before you start applying paint you have to make sure the surface is ready – clean and rugged, otherwise paint will eventually peel. That also happens when it comes to gel or acrylic; lack of preparation before the product application equals disaster.

How do you do the prep? You've got two choices here – you can do it manually using cuticle pusher and a hand file, or you can use an e-file. Whatever you prefer, just go for it. I personally like using my electric file as I find it much faster than the manual technique. Doing it manually means you have to push back the cuticle with a cuticle pusher, scrub off the pterygium with the sharp side of the pusher, file down the free edge and then etch the nail surface using a file or buffer. By using an e-file you're not only cutting the time to a minimum, but also removing the cuticle and pterygium, and etching the nail plate at the same time. It's a super bonus because you don't have to use any other tools, even for filing down the free edge. If you, for any reason, are scared to use the drill, get some training and then practice a lot on yourself to train your hand. Believe me; you're going to love this machine as *the nail techs' best friend*.

When prepping the nails with the drill, use 180 or 240 grit sanding roll and a mandrel bit. You should be changing the roll between clients, the same way you would with files. If you're right handed then set up your drill for a forward rotation (left handed – reverse) and speed between 4-6000 rotations per minute.

How to know if you're using the right speed?

Switch on the drill, grab the bit and try to stop it. If it stops then you're good to go, if doesn't and slips out from your fingers – it's too fast.

When using the e-file there's no need to push back cuticles or remove them by using cuticle nippers or any cuticle removers, unless your client's cuticles are extensively overgrown. Cuticles can be removed with the drill while prepping the whole nail. Start from the right side wall, if you're right handed, and work upwards towards the cuticle.

Then work along the cuticle

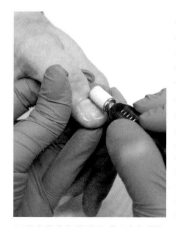

and downwards to the left side wall.

Next, remove the shine from the rest of the nail plate working in an "up and down" motion to improve adhesion.

If necessary you can use a diamond cuticle bit and go along the cuticle one more time to ensure no pterygium has been left. ALWAYS keep the bit flat to the nail to avoid any damage to the natural nail. Take your time and move slowly as this is not a race. Working safely and slowly while prepping the nail eliminates any risk of harming your customer.

There are several more aspects of natural nail preparation to remember, apart from the basic ones mentioned above. Remember:

◆ Shape of the natural free edge

As I have mentioned, you should file the natural free edge as short as possible, as you really don't need any length to apply the form underneath. If you leave some length it may actually cause you problems, especially if the edge of the nail is a funny shape, wavy, or spoon-shaped (kolionychia). When you prep a round or oval nail, you should file the sides of that nail to the highest points of the hyponychium. Not only does it help with the form application but also creates the basis for the feature smile line. The square ended nail – file it to the natural nail shape –a straight line from side to side, or you can gently round the corners and keep it as short as possible.

◆ Underneath of the natural free edge

It's very important that you file underneath the corners of the free edge. What do I mean by that? When you deal with a nail that has a very deep natural c-curve, it is very common that the side walls are deeply embedded in the skin. You have to make sure to get rid of those corners underneath or they'll be pushing the form downwards creating a gap between the form and the free edge.

◆ Prep for the classic P&W

When you do a classic P&W, with no cover pink, after etching the whole nail, you can gently buff (to eliminate deep scratches) the small margin of the free edge. That will help create a nicer and sharper smile line, as it's easier to wipe it off on the top of the smooth surface, and when product doesn't settle in the scratches.

◆ Double dehydration and primer

The standard prep procedure requires, apart from the steps already mentioned, using a dehydrator and primer. A dehydrator, such as an acetone or alcohol based liquid, cleanses the nail plate and also temporally dehydrates it, while the primer improves the adhesion by changing the pH of that plate. When dealing with a client prone to lifting, you can double dehydrate and prime the nail to ensure it will last longer with no nasty surprises – lifting.

Nail Forms -General Rules

There are many individual rules to be applied when creating a specific nail shape on a specific nail type. However, there are also some general rules you need to know and remember, no matter the shape or nail type.

♦ **Form application while creating nail shape based on a square form.**

The shape that:

- the extension edge is as narrow as the natural nail;

- doesn't taper to a pointy edge from the side wall;

- lower arch is parallel to the finger's axis and upper arch;

- Example: square, pipe, Russian almond, edge.

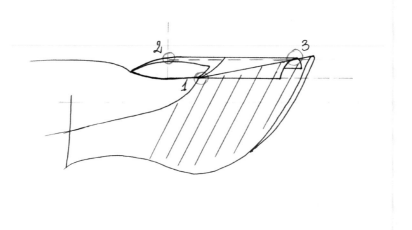

Squar'ish shapes

A form is applied parallel to the finger's axis and runs straight from the side walls (No. 1). When you start to stick together wings, then the top of the form will lift up. Your goal is to have the end of the feature extension (No. 3) as high (sometimes even slightly higher) as the apex of the natural nail (No. 2). Correct form application is when the upper arch, lower arch, and the finger's axis are parallel. The top of the form stays open.

> **SQUAR'ISH NAIL SHAPES:**
>
> **The LONGER extension the LOWER the form.**
>
> **The SHORTER extension the HIGHER the form.**

♦ **Form application while creating any nail shape based on a stiletto/ almond form.**

The type of shape that:

- side walls taper to a pointy or oval tip;

- upper arch tapers from the apex towards the free edge;

- Example: stiletto, almond, Gothic almond, ballerina shoes, aka coffin.

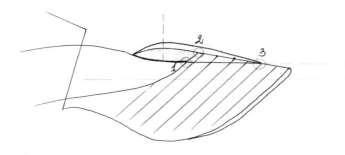

Stiletto/ Almond'ish shapes

A form is applied consistently to the natural nail curvature (No. 2) and goes downward creating a straight line from the apex to the end of the extension. The crossing point of that straight line (No. 2) and another straight line from the side wall (No.1) indicates the ending point of your future extension. If you want longer extensions then raise the form, if shorter, lower that form.

ALMOND'ISH NAIL SHAPES:

The LONGER extension the STRAIGHTER the form.

The SHORTER extension the LOWER the form.

◆ An oval free edge with overgrown hyponychium

A nail which ends in an oval/ almond shape, and has overgrown, or one that is just naturally very high hyponychium, requires form customization. If you're using an oval ending form, it still may be too flat compared to the curvature of that particular free edge shape. You'll need to cut a triangle or a U shape in the centre of the form, as shown on the photo, to ensure correct form placement.

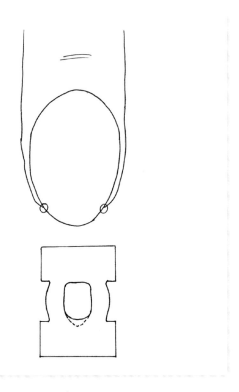

Overgrown hyponychium

This trim allows you to apply the form high enough, so the entire free edge (from the corner to the corner of the smile line) rests on the form. Always make sure you place the form on the top of the hyponychium, not under. If you apply it underneath, you'll end up with a lot of product under the natural nail. If you haven't trimmed the form, you'll have an empty gap on both side walls resulting in bad product application, and affecting the nail strength.

◆ A square free edge

This type of nail requires a little TLC when it comes to the form application. If you don't have any square ended forms handy, then you can create one for yourself. The easiest way is to cut out two small triangles, one on each side of the form – as shown in the photo.

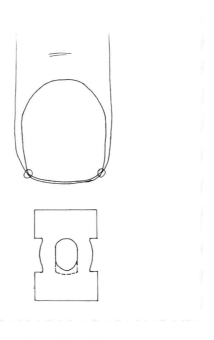

Square free edge

Start trimming down the side then to the centre, then repeat on the other side. If the natural free edge is super straight then make sure the form replicates that line, but it's quite common that even a square nail has a very gentle curve. If so, then keep the centre of the form slightly rounded to ensure a perfect fit.

◆ Puffy lateral side walls

The puffy lateral side walls and/or fingertips are like pillows around the nail plate. Unfortunately, as much as I like my pillows, these are not my favourite by any means. So, what do you do with those "pillows"? You have to make sure they're not in your way so that you have to work around them. Place the form under the free edge and check the deepest points of the smile line. From there, cut two slits (one on the left and one on the right) pointing the scissors at a 45° angle downwards. If you're able to pinch the form to make it as narrow as the nail bed, or into any desired form, then leave it like that. If not, then from the lowest point of your slit, cut what looks like a "mickey mouse ear" or "the devils horns," as shown on the photo.

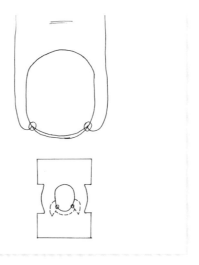

Puffy side walls

This procedure opens up the form and ensures those puffy sides won't be in your way. You can now pinch the form as narrow as you want.

◆ How to ensure a straight extension?

Many clients have a squint finger or nails (I'm one of them). Your job is to create a straight extension, which may be tricky sometimes. To make sure the feature extension is straight and looks good, you must imagine and follow the central line between the first and the second bone of the finger. This imagined line elongates over the nail and then over the form, so the middle line of the form runs consistently with the central line of the finger.

If you focus on the central line of the nail only; chances are you'll end up with each nail pointing in a different direction. Once the form is on, ask the client to turn around her hand with fingers pointing upwards. This perspective is your client's view.

This is what she sees and because our views don't always match, be sure to check with the client every time. While checking if the form is straight, don't hold her fingers, as you'll manipulate that form to see what you want to see, not how it really is. Let her straighten her fingers and then check that the central line of the finger extends to the top of the form. If everything is correct you're ready to go ahead with the product application.

◆ The wings

There's another thing to remember to ensure the correct form placement – the wings of the form. While sticking them together, always pay attention so that the wings won't overlap.

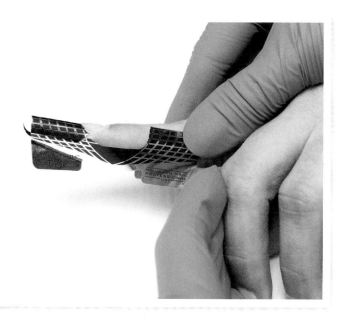

Wings of the form closed correctly

If they do, then the whole form will be twisted, as well as the extension. You don't want to see one wing lower than the other. They must be glued symmetrically.

◆ A perfect fit

The form has to lie directly underneath the free edge, on top of the hyponychium.

Perfect fit

If it's under the hyponychium and doesn't adjoin to the free edge, creating a gap, then the product will fill up that gap creating a thick, reversed "pocket" underneath. It may be uncomfortable for the client and it's also hazardous for nail infection; as bacteria or any kind of dirt may become trapped there.

Form application checklist:

✓ the form is straight to the finger

✓ there's no gap between the form and the free edge

✓ the form is applied straight or tilted downwards depending on the shape being created

✓ the free edge of the natural nail – side to side – rests on the form; the form doesn't overlap the nail

✓ the form has been cut to match the shape of the natural free edge

✓ if necessary, it has also been cut from the deepest points of smile line to allow better application

✓ the tip of the form stays open or has been closed according to specific shape requirements

✓ the wings of the form have been glued parallel and don't overlap

Pinching Techniques

There's nothing better than a beautifully structured nail and that nail is a well-pinched nail. Pinching simply means; bending the nail's c-curve in order to make it deeper. This procedure not only helps you to achieve that beautiful nail, it also makes it strong. When you look at your own natural nails from the c-curve perspective, you see that they're not flat, but curved, unless there's something odd with them, e.g. kolionychia. The extended nail must be the same. Flat nails don't last or add to glamorous hands.

As I already mentioned, the salon standard C-curve is between 25-35% of a circle, and a competition standard is as much as 50%. It can be achieved by working both on the form and the tip, using special methods.

Where and when to pinch?

When pinching the nail, you don't want to over pinch. You also shouldn't focus on the top of the free edge, as that would ruin the whole shape. The area you should be pinching is on the side wall at the deepest points of the natural nail smile line. The free edge of the extension will then curve equally.

When working with an acrylic system, you cannot rush the pinching or you'll end up with squished sides. The moment when the nail is ready, is when it's in a moulding phase. This means that when it's matt looking and no longer shiny, doesn't stick to your finger when touched, is no longer warm but still flexible, and not too soft.

The gel nail is pinched after the first layer of the gel, which creates the base of the nail, and has been flash cured. That base can be done with a clear or white gel (if working with transparent forms). Flash curing means that the gel has been frozen so it's no longer moving, but still not fully cured. That, depending on the brand, may take between 15 seconds to a minute. Also, when the final layer of gel has been applied and flash cured—you may pinch again to prevent the c-curve from getting back to its previous, flatter form.

> **To secure the c-curve and prevent it from re-straightening - apply top gel over the entire concave and cure in a lamp with hand upside-down.**

Pinching techniques

There are quite a few techniques for pinching the nail:

♦ **Use your own fingers.**

This technique can be used for both gel and acrylic. However, due to gel stickiness this wouldn't be my first choice here. Use your thumb nails to pinch the artificial nail, applying the same amount of pressure to both sides – hold it until product no longer moves.

♦ **C-curve sticks**

Thesc are metal tubes in various sizes which help to create a symmetrical c-curve.

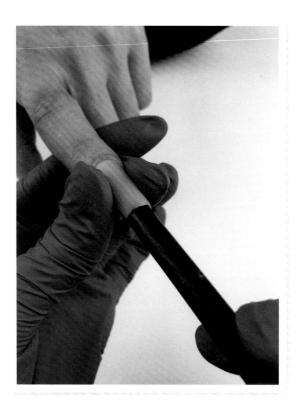

C-curve stick

Choose the correct size stick. The first stick should be as narrow as the nail. Place it under the free edge and then from the top, using your fingers, bend the product over the stick. Make sure you hold it straight without lifting the stick, as that may be painful to the customer. Once you've finished with this, choose a second stick – one size smaller than the other, then repeat this procedure until the product is set. The c-curve sticks are primarily recommended for acrylic, however, if you wish, you can also use them for the gel system.

◆ A pinching clamp

This is my favourite tool. It's made of plastic which makes it very light. I love it, because it does the trick with very little help. I like to pinch the nail with the c-curve stick or tweezers first to make sure the free edge is symmetrical, and then apply the pinching clamp from the finger side.

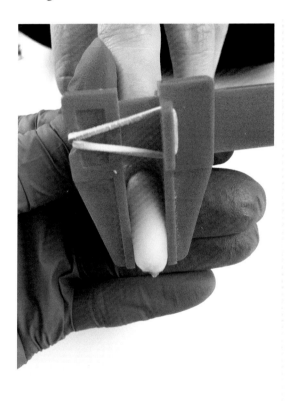

Pinching clamp

Once the clamp is on, all you need to do is to secure it tightly, then you can move on to the second nail. There's no need to hold it until the product is set. It also secures tightly, even when the client is moving her fingers. That eliminates the risk of the clamp slipping to one side and misshaping the form of the free edge. It's recommended for both gel and acrylic.

To avoid slipping off when working with gel – use a small piece of sticking plaster and glue it to the inner parts of the clamp. Its textured surface won't slip off from the gel nail. Leave it on the nail while curing under the UV light.

◆ Tweezers

You've got two choices here – manual and leave-on tweezers. The first type can be quickly used before the pinching clamp application, or after using the first size of the c-curve stick. It also can be used on its own, but then you have to hold the nail pinched until is set.

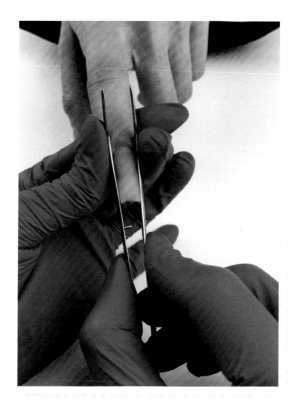

Tweezers type 1

The second type—the leave-on one, can be used the same way as the manual one, but can also be left on the nail while you work with the second nail.

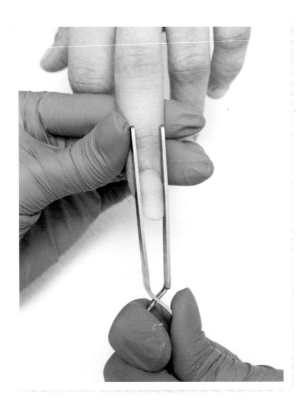

Tweezers type 2

The challenge here is that these tweezers are long and made of metal, which means they're pretty heavy. Once applied on the nail, the bottom part is resting on the table. That means the client cannot move her fingers at all as it may slip or twist the form. This is not the most comfortable scenario, but it works and gives good results.

◆ A metal badge under the form

If you'd like to spend a little bit more time on the form preparation and have amazing results, you can choose a metal badge. This piece of metal is applied under the form then bent over the correct size c-curve stick, and applied onto the nail. That ensures a symmetrical and deep c-curve without excessive pinching. That metal form, when looked after, can be used many times, so it's a very good investment.

Remember that a nice, strong nail is a pinched nail, so choose your technique and tools and start pinching, if you haven't already.

Filing Technique

—⚍—

I'm amazed how many times I hear from students in advanced classes with me, who never learned filing techniques. Do you remember when I told you that routine is our friend? Well, this is the moment when it really starts to make sense.

There are many techniques for filing, but before I teach you the one I use the most, let me explain what this term means to me. It basically means following a sequence of particular moves which are being repeated on each nail to achieve consistency..

Filing the way you like doesn't make sense, or neither brings about satisfying results. The only result you'll get is an inconsistent set of nails; where each nail looks like it's been living its own life.

Let's talk first about the tools you'll need — **files and buffers.**

A File is one of the most important tools that nail technicians use and need, but do you actually know enough about them? Let me to make it clear before moving on and answering the most common questions about files and buffers.

I'm sure you've seen the printed numbers on almost every file on the market. If both numbers are the same that means both sides are the same grit; two different numbers; two different sides. OK, but what do those numbers mean?

Let's take 180/180 for example; that means both sides are the same. It also means that there are **180 grits per 1 square centimetre**. Now, knowing that, you can clearly understand which file is sharper and which one less corrosive.

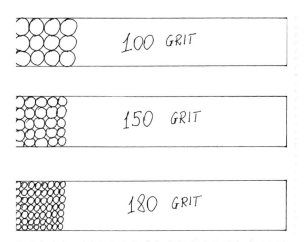

Simply saying – the higher the number – the less corrosive file; the lower the number, the sharper file.

- **80/80 grit** is the sharpest file you can find on the market (1 square centimetre contains 80 pretty large grits). This file is used for product removal. It allows you to file off lots of product quickly. However, keep in mind that you're *never ever* allowed to over file the nail, so don't use 80 grit when the product is very thin. Also remember that gel is easier to file than acrylic, so reduce the pressure adequately.

- **100 grit** – used to take the length down, shape side walls, and the free edge. I wouldn't recommend using this grit to file the nail surface as it creates deep scratches, which means more buffing later on.

- **150 grit** – used to file nail surface and shape the entire nail. You can also use it to remove any lifting prior to the new product application.

- **180 grit** – used to contour the whole nail; to prep the natural nail before applying any product, and also to shorten or shape the natural free edge.

- **240 grit** – used to prep nails, especially before a UV gel polish application; due to its low corrosive surface.

Buffers – these have numbers too, just like the files. However, they're made of a board, sanding paper and a sponge, which makes them more delicate and softer than a hard file. Use buffers to bring the shine to acrylic or natural nails.

- **100/180 grit buffer** should be used first in order to make acrylic nails shiny. Start with the lowest buffer number and work towards the highest one. The 180 grit side may also be used to prep a natural nail before the UV gel polish application. This particular buffer eliminates scratches that appear following the use of the hard file.

- **220/280 grit** – this is your second step. During the manicure, you can use this buffer to eliminate ridges from natural nails; making them even and smooth prior to nail polish application. It eliminates scratches on acrylic nails after usage of 100/180 grit one.

- **600/4000 grit** – this is a magic wand that brings the shine up. Most of the   brands have one side in green and another in white. Many people concentrate on the white side ignoring the green, while it's the green one that creates the shine. The white one only reveals it. So to have a beautiful, mirror glass shine, make sure you do a really good job with the green side.

The extremely important thing to always remember is to prepare your file before the first usage. Sides/ edges of the new file are sharp like a knife and could easily cut clients' cuticle or side walls. ALWAYS get rid of those sharp edges! Use two files and file edge on edge to bold them slightly.

Does file shape matter? Not really. You can find various shapes: straight (wild and slim), half-moon, diamond, banana etc. It's really up to you which one you want to use. I personally like   the half-moon shape when working around the cuticle area, as it lowers the risk of cutting or irritating them. Straight file is the best for filing free edge, side walls and lower arch; it makes it easier to get a nice and straight shape.

Is it worth it to pay a bit more for a file? Yes, it is. Files can be disinfected and used more than once, unless they were in contact with blood or any type of bacteria. Having said that I would recommend you get a good quality, branded files which cost a bit more, but also last longer than cheap files. They're also stronger and don't bend during filing which makes your job much easier and more pleasant for you and your client. Cheap files are very likely to separate from the board during or after being disinfected. How to disinfect the file? Simply brush off the dust using your ordinary manicure brush, wash it with a hint of soap and then spray or soak with a disinfectant liquid and let it dry. Buying good files will save you money in the end.

Remember that every file, no matter how good and strong, is not going to last forever and after a while you'll have to exchange it. The moment to do so is when you notice that filing takes you longer than usual and instead of filing you're buffing the nail.

"10-step Filing Technique" step by step

———ᘰᘰᘰ———

Like I said before, there are many filing techniques you can juggle between. The most important thing here is to choose one and stick to it while filing that particular set of nails. The last thing you want (as well as your client) is to have 10 odd shapes in one set.

Here is my 10-step salon Filing Technique for the majority of nail shapes using 150 or 180 grit file:

1. Hold the file upright to **the free edge**.

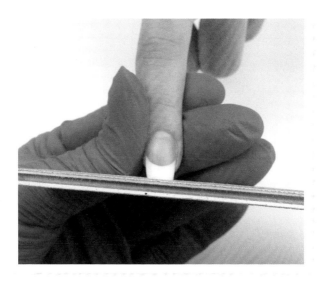

File from the left to the right until you're happy with the length and when the free edge is straight. If the client doesn't like sharp corners and wants a softer finish, then angle the file under the free edge at about 20-30° and file.

2. File **the side walls**.

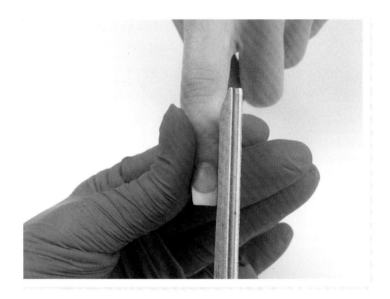

Place the file into the nail and hold it parallel to the side wall. Imagine you're holding a saw and can only move up and down. Bracing your hand will help with holding the file upright and eliminate unnecessary moves to the side. Holding the file the same way, angle it towards the centre of the nail at about 20° and file up and down again.

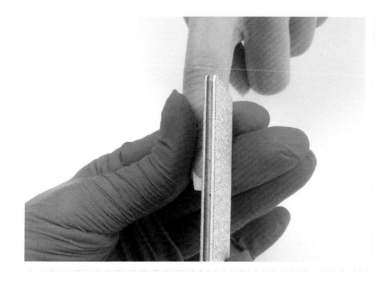

That will file off any bulkiness from the side walls and begin contouring the nail.

3. Repeat step 2 on the opposite side.

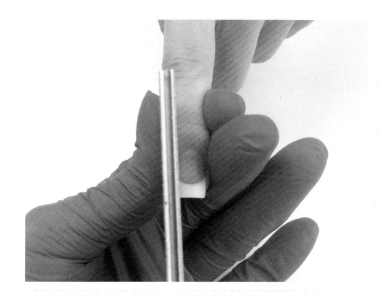

4. The lower arch.

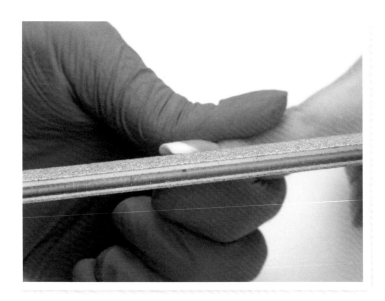

Hold the file upright to the side wall and now change the angle, moving it 45° to the side. Place it flat under the free edge making sure it's parallel to the finger's axis and upper arch. File in an up-down motion from the deepest point of the side wall to the end of the free edge. Make sure not to over file the contact area (the deepest point of the hyponychium and also the beginning of the extension).

5. File **the lower arch** on the second side.

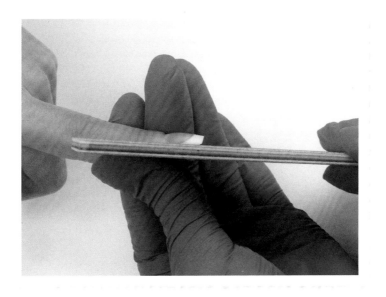

6. Focus on contouring **the side wall**.

Start with the left side and file the product upwards to ¼ of the centre of the nail in a curvy move. Work from the tip towards the cuticle area.

7. File **the cuticle area** holding the file flat, a maximum angle at 20°, as that helps to establish the apex and protects the natural nail from any damage at the same time.

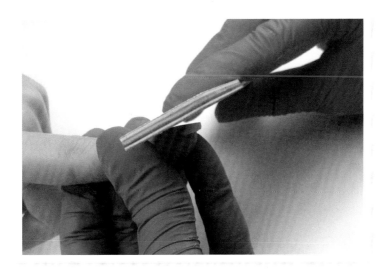

File along the cuticle line starting from the left side (if you're right-handed), working towards the centre and then downwards to the right. Next go back to the centre of the cuticle and file from there— downwards to the left, then downwards to the right. The cuticle line extends to the side line and is filed downwards up to the free edge of the natural nail point. That will "close" the side walls, making them flash to the natural nail.

8. Contour **the right side wall**.

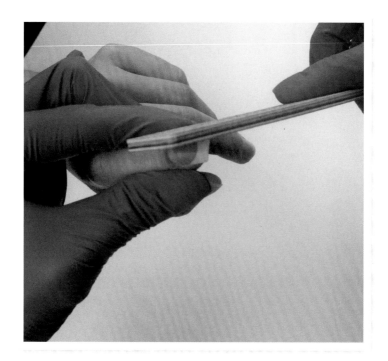

Turn the hand to the side and file the nail upwards from the bottom of the side wall. Focus on filing ¼ of the right side wall. File from the extension's tip towards the cuticle line.

9. File **the surface of the nail**.

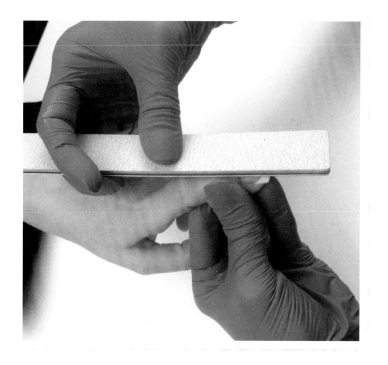

Hold the file flat/ parallel to the nail. You must never change that angle. Your hand is from the client's side so you file towards yourself and the free edge. Start at the centre then keep moving to the left side first (if you're right-handed) using the up-down motion. When you move to the left your elbow goes up, so the file is in constant contact with the nail surface ensuring the correct shape of the extension. Once you've reached the left side wall, start filing back towards the centre and from there to the right side - your elbow goes down.

10. **The apex** has been established, not only by the product application, but also by filing pretty flat around the cuticle area and completely flat on the top of the nail.

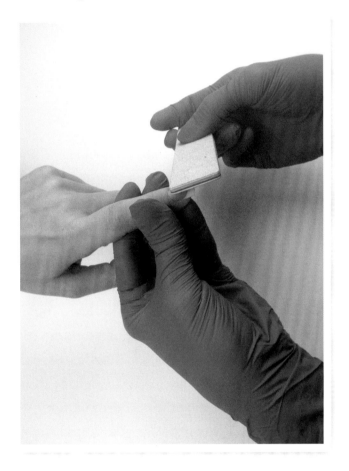

Now, all you have to do is to go back there and smooth any imperfections so it has a nice arch and no bulkiness.

10-step Filing Technique quick guide:

1. Free edge

2. 1st side wall

3. 2nd side wall

4. 1st lower arch

5. 2nd lower arch

6. Contour 1st side

7. Cuticle line

8. Contour 2nd side

9. Surface of the nail

10. Apex

To finish the nail you can choose between two methods. You can buff the nail to a high shine using buffers and the system I've already described. Another, easier way, is to apply the gel top coat, but before you do you may smooth the nail with 180 grit buffer to ensure a nicer finish.

Product Application

In this chapter I'll explain the general rules of product application. These are the techniques I use on a daily basis when working with customers and teaching my students. These are also the techniques I used in my online training, which shows a step-by-step of every procedure described in this book. So if you'd like to watch, not only read about it, then this training is just perfect for you.

Before you apply any product make sure the nail prep has been done and forms applied.

If you're using a gel system which requires a base gel, then start with that. The gel system I'm using doesn't require any of these, which is why I start with clear gel application straight away.

The techniques below explain:

- Classic acrylic P&W – 3 beads technique

- Classic gel P&W

- Acrylic natural look – 2 beads technique

- Gel natural look technique

- Acrylic P&W with nail bed elongation

- Gel P&W with nail bed elongation – Pure White technique

- Gel P&W with nail bed elongation – Classic technique

- UV Gel Polish application over gel or acrylic

These are techniques I used to create my eight shapes based on three nail types. I've mixed them up, so you can see the same nail shape done with both gel or acrylic, and its variations. These are also the general rules of product application, which I customized later on in order to create a desired shape.

> **Remember - sculpt with the brush not with the file!**

♦ Classic acrylic P&W – 3-beads technique

1. Pick up the white bead – the size of the bead depends on the size of the nail and extension length. Place that bead on the middle of the form close to the natural free edge. Press that bead gently in the centre to spread it equally. Using the belly of the brush press the product from the centre to the right corner, then from

the centre to the left. Using the tip, guide the product to the corners of the free edge to deepen the smile line. Make sure the lower arch of the extension is straight and runs consistently with the nail growth. Clean behind the smile line working from the centre to right corner, then centre to left corner.

How to achieve a crispy smile line:

Make sure the smile line creates an even "wall." to prevent the pink from going over the white, and to give you a sharp smile line after the nail has been filed.

If the white was flash to the nail plate, then pink would create dark shadows over the entire extension edge.

2. Using transparent pink, apply a medium-size bead to the middle of the nail. Press it from side to side to build the apex and gently feather the rest of it over the extension edge. Make sure the product along the side walls creates a clean thin edge without touching the skin.

3. Apply a small bead of transparent pink to the cuticle area. Work it from side to side and blend over the previous bead. This application should create a tapered line from the stress area (second bead) to a thin edge along the cuticle area. Smooth the entire nail with several brush strokes.

◆ Classic gel P&W

1. Brush on a thin layer of gel over the nail plate and create a thin extension using clear gel. Make sure there are no dents over the entire extension edge. Flash cure and pinch.

2. Using you chosen white, apply the product between the free edge of the natural nail and the form. Massage the gel from the centre to right corner, then centre to left one. Stroke the product over the entire free edge and smooth it. Clean the brush and wipe off the smile line. Cure

Two techniques for wiping off the smile line:

1. **ONE MOVE – start from the left corner (if you're right-handed). Using a square brush place it flat to the nail just in front of the white product. Use only the corner of the brush to wipe off the smile line across to the centre, then twist the brush a bit and go upwards to the second corner.**

2. **TWO MOVES – start from the centre and using just the corner of the flat brush, wipe off the smile line across to the right corner, and then to the left. Make sure both points of the smile line are symmetrical.**

3. Using a builder clear or clear gel, brush a thin layer over the whole nail. Don't cure and pick up the "builder layer." Place that gel near the cuticle area and gently blend towards it. Next, massage it towards the free edge. Make sure the application is smooth to avoid heavy filling. Double check to see if the structure has been created. Cure.

> **Use gravity to create the upper arch:**
>
> **Take the hand upside-down and let the product run freely. Control the apex and move the product into place, if necessary, using your brush.**

4. Wipe off the sticky layer, file, and buff with 180 grit buffer. Remove the dust, apply top gel and cure.

◆ Acrylic natural look – 2-beads technique

1. Use a medium size bead of a natural acrylic powder to create the extension's edge. Place it on the form close to the natural free edge and pat it from side to side creating desired length.

2. Use a larger bead and place it 1/3 away from the cuticle area. Gently pat it along the cuticle line (should be flash to the natural nail), and then stroke it towards the free edge ensuring the correct structure has been created. If you need to add more beads, then go for it. Also, if you cannot get the correct structure with just two

beads, then use a 3 bead application: 1st applied to the free edge zone – 2nd to the stress zone – and 3rd to the cuticle zone. You can also do the whole extension using the one bead technique, which is really fast, but requires some practice.

3. After pinching, filing, and buffing, apply the colour or create some nail art, such as a one stroke design. If you'd like to learn more about one stroke painting visit my page **www.elaloszczyk.co.uk**

♦ Gel natural look technique

1. Apply a thin layer of your chosen gel (clear, pink, milky pink, natural) over the nail plate. Next, create a thin extension on the form. Flash cure and pinch.

2. Brush on a thin layer of the same gel and without curing between layers, add a "builder layer" to create the correct structure. Place that bead on the stress area and gently massage around the cuticle area, then stroke it towards the free edge. Cure.

> **How to avoid that burning sensation while curing gel under the UV lamp:**
>
> 1. Place the hand in front of the lighted lamp. Hold it like that for 15 seconds then put the hand to the lamp for 3 seconds. Next, take it back to where it was.
> 2. Repeat that procedure three times.
> 3. After the third time, place the hand under the lamp for required amount of time.

3. Wipe off the sticky residue, file, buff, and remove the dust. Apply UV Gel Polish or top gel and cure.

◆ Acrylic P&W with nail bed elongation

1. Use a medium size cover pink to elongate the nail bed. Remove the excess liquid from the bead and apply that bead behind the natural sile line, in the middle of the form. Press it to the left corner, then to right and blend to the nail plate. Correct the smile line. Pat the product from the side to the centre (repeat on the opposite side) and then stroke it. Work with the smile line until it stops moving.

2. Pick up a small bead and without wiping off the excess liquid apply behind the first bead and blend it. Don't cover the lunula in order to achieve a natural look.

3. Using transparent pink, create the correct structure and thin cuticle area.

4. Wait until the elongation is dry and without removing the form, file the smile line. Remove the dust using your manicure brush or an acrylic brush and monomer.

When filing the smile line, never press the file against the form, as it will create a gap and white acrylic will leak underneath.

5. Apply white acrylic to create the extension. Press the bead from side to side and push it to the corners of the smile line. Add more white product if necessary. If the product application is correct, there's no need to use any clear acrylic between the white and pink.

6. Pinch the c-curve, file, buff and apply top gel. Cure and massage cuticle oil into cuticles and hyponychium.

◆ Gel P&W with nail bed elongation – Pure White technique

1. Start by brushing a thin layer of gel over the nail plate and then create a clear extension on the form to a desired length. This base layer should be applied sparsely at the extension edge. The majority of the product is behind the natural free edge to ensure an even surface without any dents. Flash cure for 15 – 20 seconds, then pinch using tweezers and pinching tool. Leave the pinching tool on and put the finger back under the lamp to ensure the gel has been fully cured.

2. Using a cover pink, elongate the nail bed leaving the majority of the product on the smile line area. Cure.

3. Apply transparent or milky pink over the cover pink creating the correct structure. The product should be applied straight from the apex to the smile line. Cure.

4. Wipe off the sticky layer and using a hand file or electric drill, file and sharpen the smile line. Ensure corners are finished to a sharp point too.

> You'll achieve a sharper smile line and whiter free edge by using pink and white gel to create the structure. Using a lot of clear on top of the white may turn it yellow.

5. Depending on the white gel, apply one or two layers (cure between) to the extension edge. Push the product against the smile line wall and brush over the edge. Repeat the application if necessary. Make sure the application is smooth and even and don't worry if the white gel is over the pink. Cure

6. Don't apply any clear over the nail because the structure has already been created with the pink gel. Wipe off the sticky residue, then file, buff, apply the top gel and cure it.

◆ Gel P&W with nail bed elongation – Classic technique

This nail structure is done with a clear gel.

1. Use the same technique as described in "Gel P&W with nail bed elongation – pure white technique" to create the base layer using clear gel. Cure.

2. Create the nail bed elongation and structure the same way it was used in the previous technique.

3. Wipe off the sticky layer and file the smile line.

4. Apply white gel to the free edge. This gel is evenly applied and there's no white over the pink. If you need to, clean the smile line. Cure.

5. Use builder or clear gel to create the structure: paint over a thin amount first to make the entire surface even more slippery (the next layer will spread quicker and easier). Without curing in between, apply the "builder layer." Pick up a bigger scoop and place it on the apex area, then massage it gently towards the free edge, ensuring the structure is correct. Cure.

6. Next, wipe off the sticky layer and file using your chosen filing technique, or use the one I'm teaching in this book.

♦ UV Gel Polish application over gel or acrylic

The UV Gel Polish application over the gel or acrylic depends on the type of the product you're using. According to the manufacturer, you may apply one or two coats. If two coats are required, then cure between each layer. Next, apply top gel and cure. Once cured, wipe off the tacky layer.

There's no need to apply a UV gel polish Base Gel on top of the acrylic or gel extension.

NOTES:

_____

_____

_____

_____

_____

_____

_____

_____

_____

_____

_____

_____

_____

Part III

8/3

This part of the book is your *HOW TO*.

I'll show you, step by step, the differences in the form and product application. I'll also explain exactly what to do when it comes to customizing the form depending on the type of the natural nail you're working with, and the shape you're creating.

I've based all my shapes on three natural nail types (already mentioned at the beginning of the book):

🌢 Standard

🌢 Hooked

🌢 Bitten

The nail shapes I've chosen to teach are:

🌢 Perfect square

🌢 Pipe

🌢 Stiletto

🌢 Almond

🌢 Russian almond

🌢 Merilyn

🌢 Gothic almond

🌢 Edge

I've already showed you my most common filing technique, which is the same for majority of these shapes. However, some adjustments may be needed here and there. Don't worry; I've covered these as well in order to make it as simple as possible for you. Not to forget that the product application covers acrylic and gel, natural looking, and P&W extensions to give you a full package.

Let's get busy with the first shape - Perfect square.

Perfect Square shape

The Square shape is one of the oldest, yet still most popular nail shapes as it looks good in a long or short version.

What I'm presenting you here is a MODERN square shape on three different types of natural nails, but you can see that the final result is pretty much the same. The shape and structure remains the same for all.

The extension's edge is as narrow as the nail and finishes in a straight line. Lower arches are parallel and run straight from the side walls. That's the characteristic of a square nail extension.

Standard nail - Classic acrylic P&W

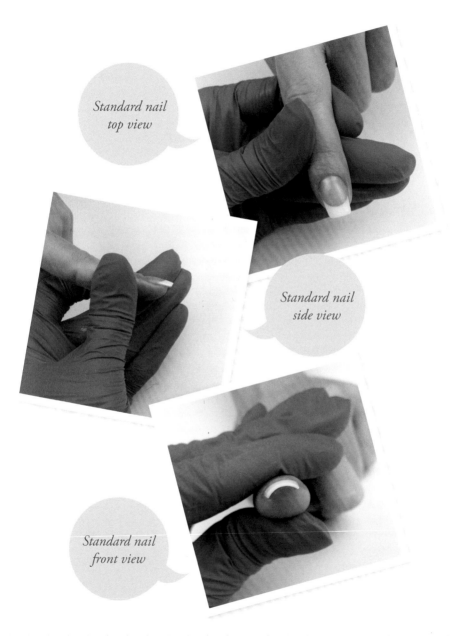

Standard nail
top view

Standard nail
side view

Standard nail
front view

Hooked nail - Gel P&W with nail bed elongation - Pure White technique

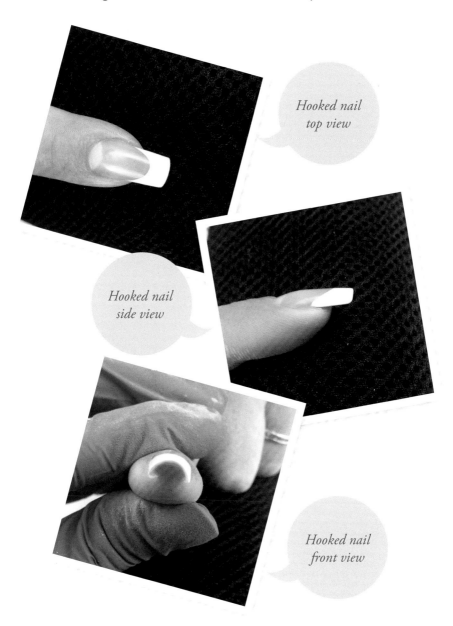

Hooked nail
top view

Hooked nail
side view

Hooked nail
front view

Bitten nail - Acrylic natural look - 2 beds technique

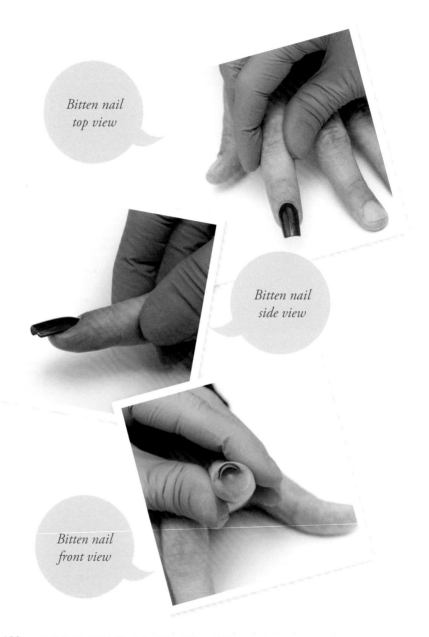

Bitten nail
top view

Bitten nail
side view

Bitten nail
front view

Form application

The form is applied according to the general principles I've described before. There are small differences between each nail, which I'll point out now.

The form is applied as high as the apex or slightly higher, so on the standard nail it will be straight or slightly lifted; on a hookcd one, it will be lifted up quite a lot (depending on the height of the natural apex); nail biter – will be straight or lifted also.

Standard nail side view

Hooked nail side view

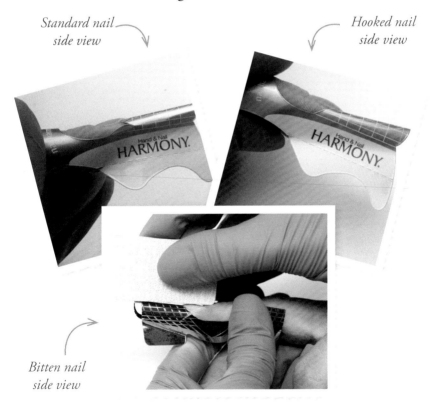

Bitten nail side view

The tip of the form stays open. It's round on the standard and bitten nail, but shaped like a tear drop on the hooked nail. To achieve that, gently roll the form between your thumbs without bending it, then apply under the free edge. The form is as narrow as the nail.

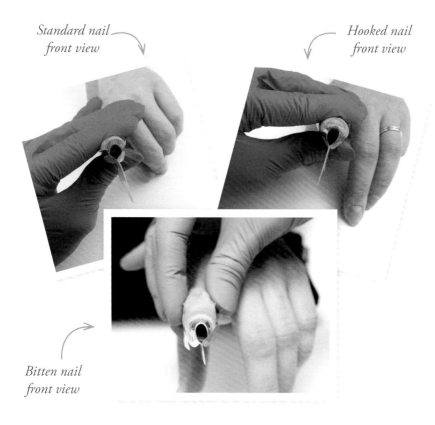

Standard nail front view

Hooked nail front view

Bitten nail front view

The form is straight to the finger and customized to fit nicely around the fingertip and free edge.

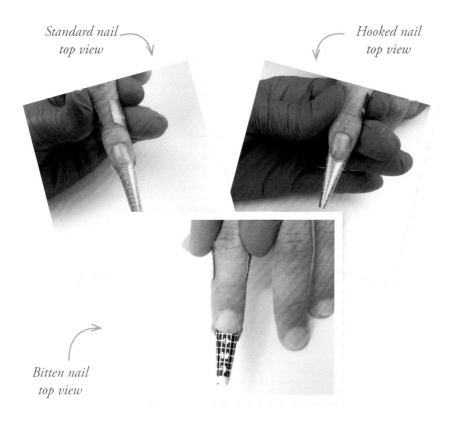

Standard nail top view

Hooked nail top view

Bitten nail top view

Make sure that all the form application checklist points have been ticked.

Product application

- The product is applied according to the general rules.

- Free edge is straight.

- Lower arch, upper arch, and finger axis is parallel.

- The apex is on 1/3 or between 1/3 – 2/3 away from the cuticle.

- Standard nail – product is balanced over the entire nail.

- Hooked nail – the majority of product is in the middle of the nail, on the top of the natural free edge where nail is the lowest.

- Nail biter – the majority of the product is on the nail plate over the apex to balance the nail and create a straight application from the apex to the extension's edge.

Filing technique

When filing the square shape follow the 10-step Filing Technique.

Pipe shape

The Pipe shape, a close cousin to the square shape, looks more delicate and feminine.

You can create a pipe shape from the square shape simply by filing the extension's edge to a 45° angle. You can also create the pipe free edge right away on the form, and that's what I'm going to show you here. The only difference between this shape and the square nail is that the free edge is angled.

Standard nail - Acrylic P&W with nail bed elongation

Standard nail
top view

Standard nail
side view

Standard nail
front view

Hooked nail - Gel P&W with nail bed elongation - Classic technique

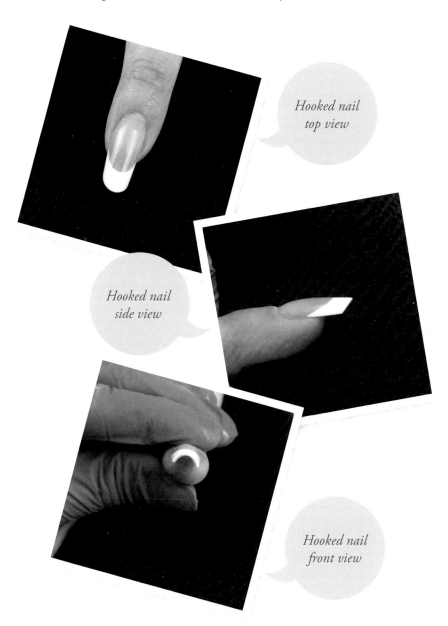

Hooked nail
top view

Hooked nail
side view

Hooked nail
front view

Bitten nail - Acrylic natural look - 2 beads technique

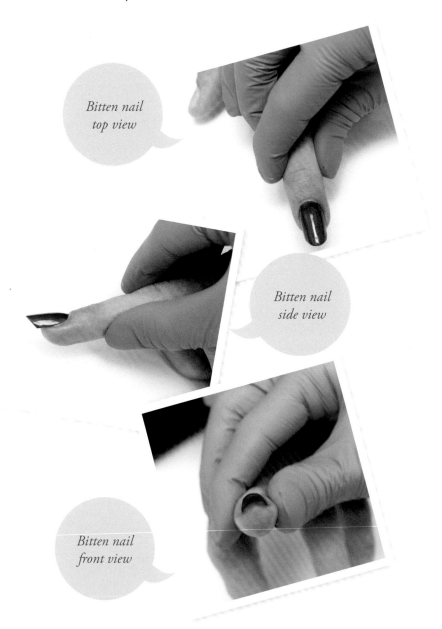

Bitten nail
top view

Bitten nail
side view

Bitten nail
front view

Form application

The form application is similar to the square shape with some small adjustments.

The form is applied as high, or slightly higher than the natural nail apex, so when you join the apex point with the end of the feature extension, the line will be parallel to the finger and lower arch. The end of the extended nail on the standard nail will be higher than the natural nail apex. On a hooked nail—lifted as high as the natural apex; nail biter—will be lifted up slightly too.

Standard nail side view

Hooked nail side view

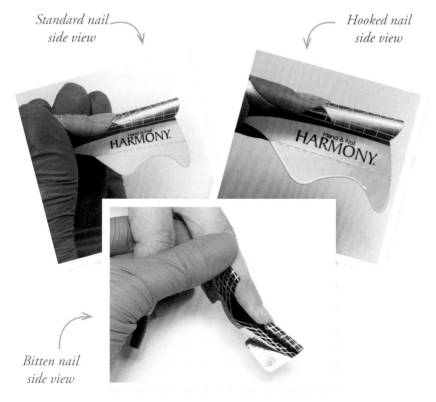

Bitten nail side view

The tip of the form stays open and creates a tear drop on all types of nails due to the form being lifted up. After rolling the form between your fingers, you can also bend it slightly in the centre (don't create a defined edge), so the c-curve will be deeper. The form is as narrow as the nail.

Standard nail front view

Hooked nail front view

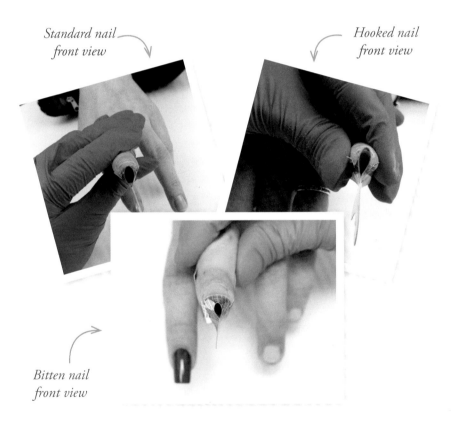

Bitten nail front view

The form is applied straight to the finger and customized to fit nicely around the fingertip and free edge.

Standard nail top view

Hooked nail top view

Bitten nail top view

Follow the form application checklist too.

Product application

- Apply the first bead to create a typical pipe shape edge – the tip is rounded in the middle and then "cut" at a 45° angle across to the side wall.

- The side walls are straight and parallel to the upper arch and finger.

- The upper arch runs in a straight line from the apex to the extension's edge.

- The apex is on 1/3 or between 1/3 – 2/3 away from the cuticle.

- Standard nail – the nail is easy to balance because product application is even.

- Hooked nail – the majority of the product is in the middle of the nail. There's just a very small amount over the natural apex. The nail looks thin, but this is just a visual effect.

- Nail biter – most of the product is applied over the apex to build up the height and to balance the structure.

Filing technique

Follow the 10-step Filing Technique.

The difference here is in filing the tip:

- file the free edge at a 45° angle to create a characteristic pipe shape tip.

Stiletto shape

A stiletto shape ends in a pointy tip and can do magic on someone with short fingers, because it visually elongates them, so they look more delicate. In contrary to appearances this is a very comfortable shape. The only problem may be the length, but this could be easily customized.

The length of the stiletto shape depends on the length of a natural nail—the longer the nail, the longer the extension. Never create extensions that are too long or extremely short, and remember to adjust the height of the apex to the length.

Standard nail - Acrylic P&W with nail bed elongation

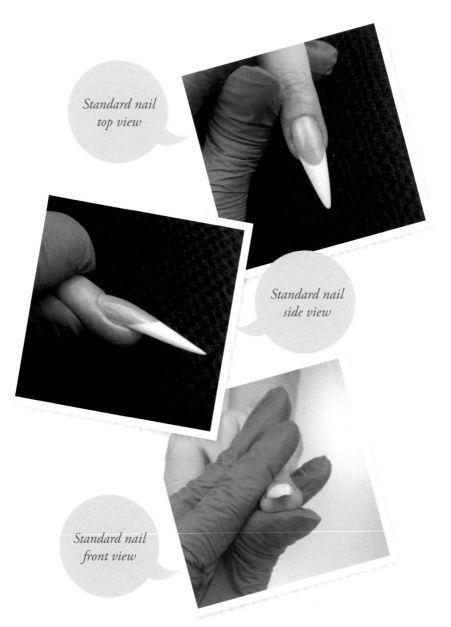

Standard nail
top view

Standard nail
side view

Standard nail
front view

Hooked nail - Gel P&W with nail bed elongation - Pure White technique

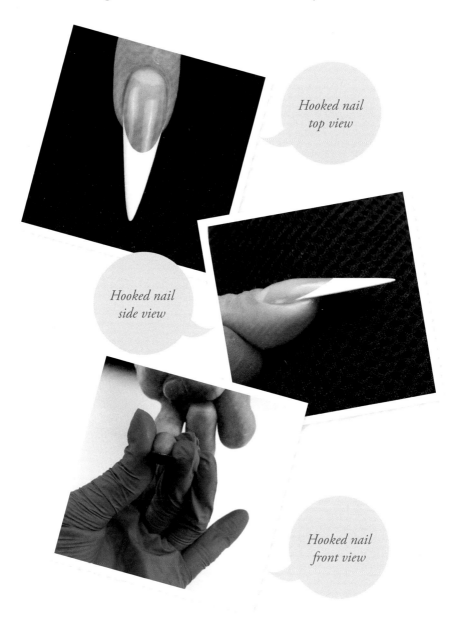

Hooked nail top view

Hooked nail side view

Hooked nail front view

Bitten nail - Acrylic natural look technique

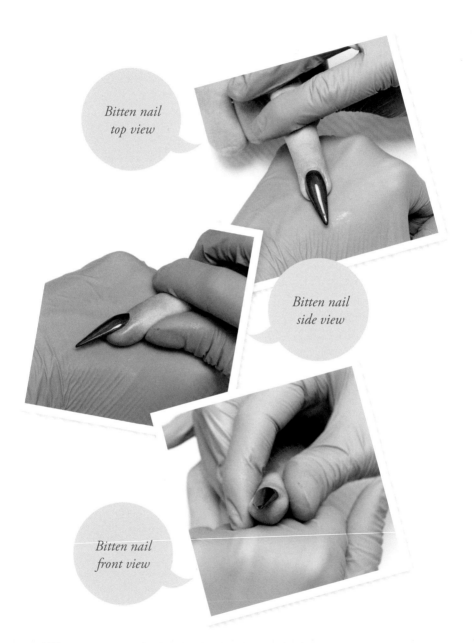

Bitten nail
top view

Bitten nail
side view

Bitten nail
front view

Form application

The form is applied consistently with the natural nail curvature, which means tilting downwards. Remember that the longer extension form is straighter to the finger's axis; the shorter extension, the lower the form. If the form was applied straight, or higher than the apex on a short extension, then the lower arch would be going upwards, which is not the shape of a typical stiletto nail.

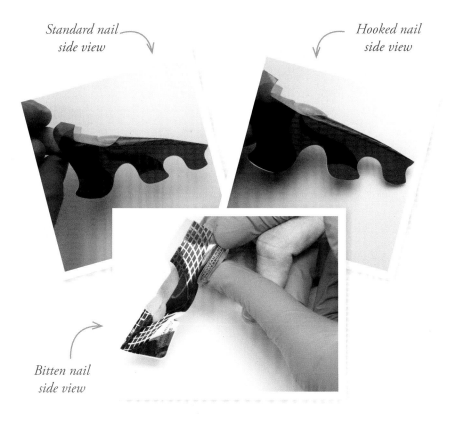

Standard nail side view

Hooked nail side view

Bitten nail side view

The tip of the form is completely closed. You can use standard or stiletto forms, but if the extension is shorter than the form, pinch the tip of that form to a desired length. That will create a better shape to the nail. The form creates a very pointy stiletto shape.

Standard nail front view

Hooked nail front view

Bitten nail front view

The form fits nicely under the free edge and around the fingertip.

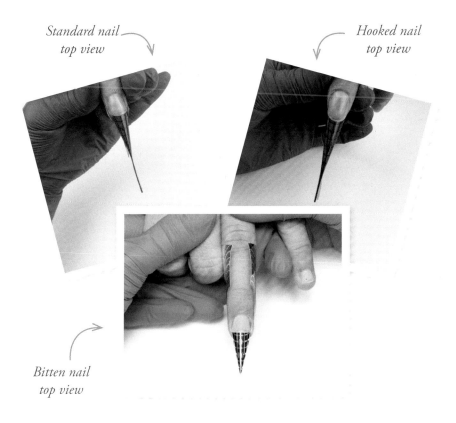

Standard nail top view

Hooked nail top view

Bitten nail top view

Make sure the general rules have been applied.

Product application

- The free edge creates a stiletto shape.

- Lower arch runs from side walls into a pointy tip.

- The extension can end in a pointy tip or gently rounded, to be more manageable.

- The apex is between 1/3 - 2/3 away from the cuticle area.

- Standard and hooked nail – the product application is the same. The majority of the product stays over the apex.

- Hooked nail – the majority of product is on the top of the natural nail's free edge, and layered very thin over the natural apex.

Filing technique

The 10-step Filing technique applies.

<u>The differences here are:</u>

- Gently round the tip of extension as there's no straight line in the free edge

- File the side wall straight from the highest points of the smile line to the tip, keeping the file angled.

- Make sure the pointy tip is exactly in the centre of the nail.

- The nail goes downwards from the apex, so make sure you file the nail accordingly. Place the file flat on the surface of the nail and file in an up-and-down motion.

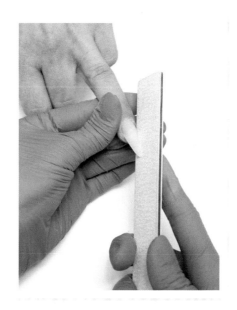

Shape the side walls

File lower arch

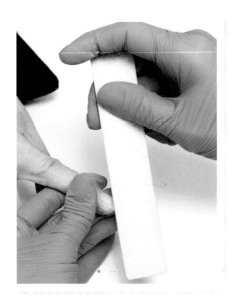

Contour the nail sides

File cuticle area

Shape the top of the nail and smooth the apex

Almond shape

—⁓⁓⁓—

The Almond shape is a mini version of a stiletto shape. However, apart from being shorter, most of the time, it is also not as pointy as the stiletto. This is one of the most comfortable shapes to be worn on a daily basis.

Standard nail - Acrylic P&W with nail bed elongation

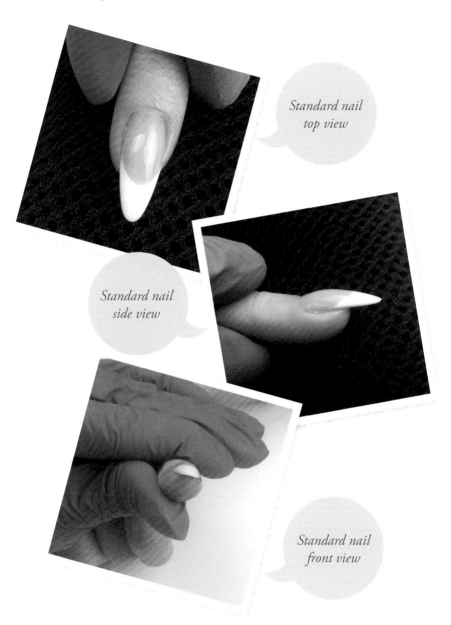

Standard nail
top view

Standard nail
side view

Standard nail
front view

Hooked nail - Gel P&W with nail bed elongation - Pure White technique

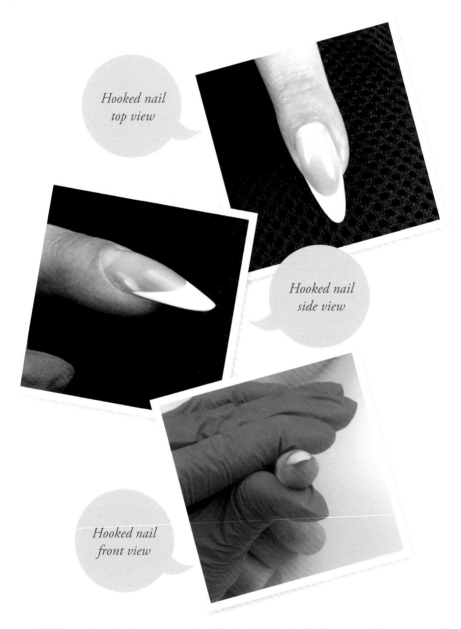

Hooked nail top view

Hooked nail side view

Hooked nail front view

Bitten nail - Acrylic natural look technique

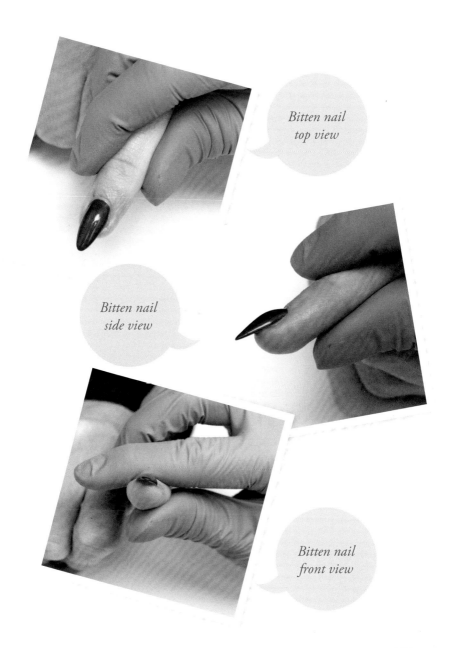

Bitten nail
top view

Bitten nail
side view

Bitten nail
front view

Form application

The form is applied downwards and runs consistently with the curvature of the natural nail. Depending on the extension's length, keep the form straight, or lower, than the apex.

Standard nail side view

Hooked nail side view

Bitten nail side view

The tip of the form is pinched and closed completely if the extension is short, staying slightly open when creating a longer elongation. The form is as narrow as the nail under the free edge and closes towards the tip creating a soft stiletto shape.

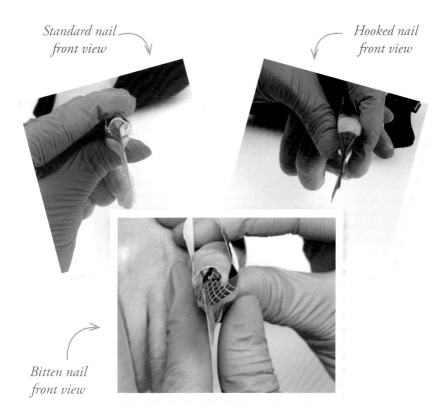

Standard nail front view

Hooked nail front view

Bitten nail front view

The form is customized to fit around the fingertip and the curvature of the natural free edge.

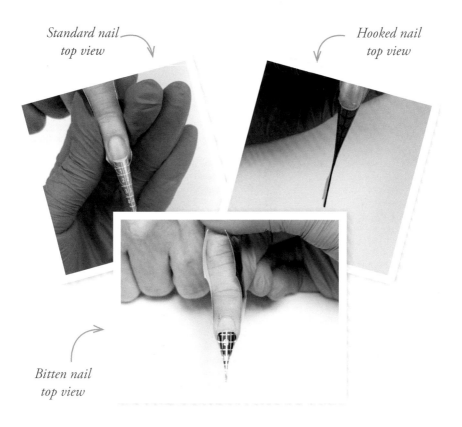

Standard nail
top view

Hooked nail
top view

Bitten nail
top view

Follow the general rules of form application as well.

Product application

- The free edge creates a very soft and rounded stiletto shape.

- Lower arch runs in a straight line from side walls to a rounded tip.

- The apex is between 1/3 - 2/3 away from the cuticle area.

- The nail goes downward from the apex to the extension's edge.

- Standard and hooked nail – the product application is the same as the stiletto nail. The majority of the product stays over the apex.

- Hooked nail – the majority of the product is on the top of the natural nail's free edge, and only a very thin layer over the natural apex.

Filing technique

File it using the 10-step Filing technique.

Here are the differences:

- Round the tip of the extension; so it's not pointy like a stiletto;

- File the side walls from the highest points of the smile line to the tip, creating an almond shape.

- The tip of the almond nail is exactly in the centre of the nail.

- The nail goes downwards from the apex to the tip. Divide the natural nail length into three equal parts, then file the extension's surface straight to the tip starting from first 1/3 point (when viewed from the tip).

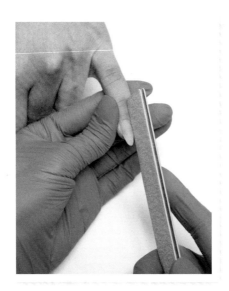

Shape the side walls

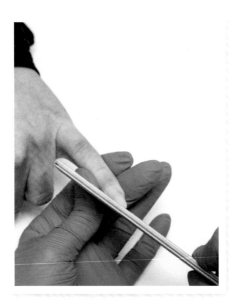

Shape the side walls on opposite side

File lower arch and contour the nail

Blend cuticle area

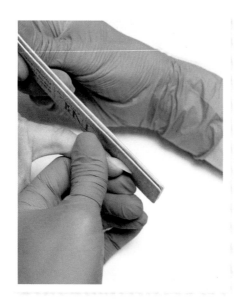

File the top of the nail and the apex

Russian Almond

This is my favourite shape. It's got all the advantages of a square and almond nail, beautifully merged in one nail. This shape looks better when it's longer, but the shorter version is also nice.

Standard nail - Gel natural look technique

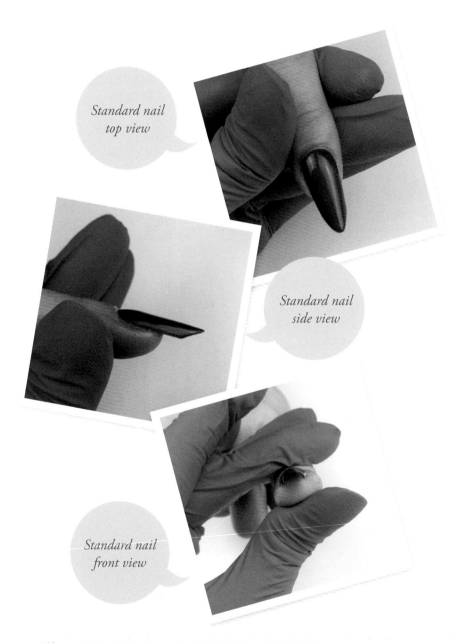

Standard nail
top view

Standard nail
side view

Standard nail
front view

Hooked nail - Acrylic P&W (in color) with nail bed elongation

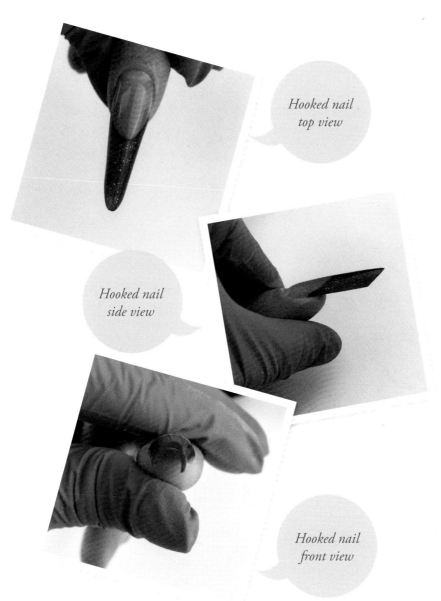

Hooked nail top view

Hooked nail side view

Hooked nail front view

Bitten nail - Acrylic natural look technique

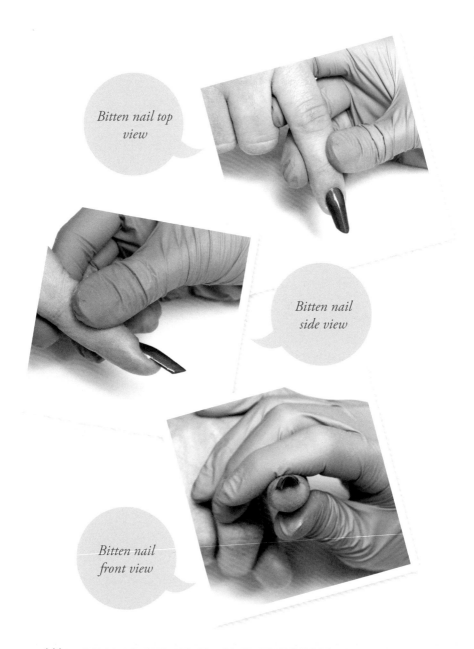

Bitten nail top view

Bitten nail side view

Bitten nail front view

Form application

The form is applied according to the general principles with some differences.

The form should be applied as high as the apex or higher. The form on a standard nail will be lifted; on a hooked one it will be lifted up as high as the apex; on a nail biter it will be lifted slightly higher than the apex.

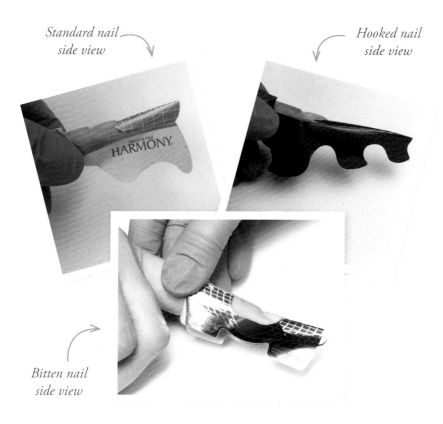

Standard nail side view

Hooked nail side view

Bitten nail side view

The tip of the form is open and creates a tear drop on all type of nails. The higher you lift the form the smaller the tear drop. To achieve that gentle roll, put the form between your thumbs and bend it in the middle without creating a sharp edge, then apply under the free edge. The form is as narrow as the nail and closes into a soft stiletto shape.

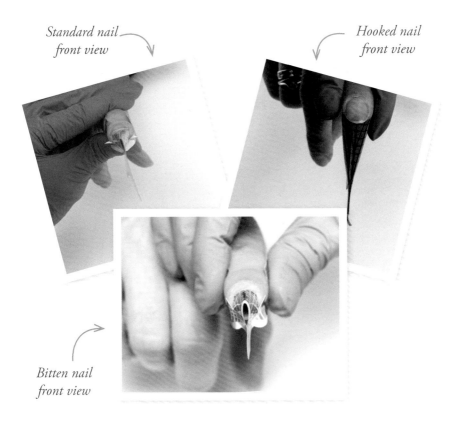

Standard nail front view

Hooked nail front view

Bitten nail front view

The form is straight to the finger and customized to fit nicely around the fingertip and the free edge.

Standard nail top view

Hooked nail top view

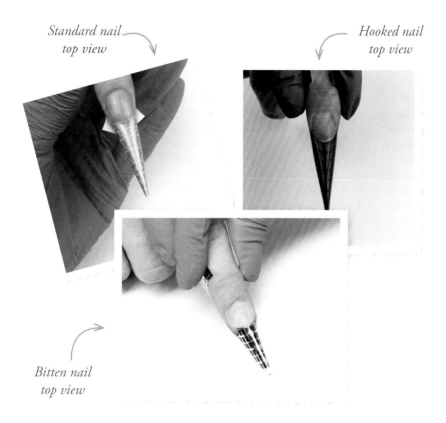

Bitten nail top view

Remember about the form checklist points.

Product application

- The general rules apply.

- The free edge runs in a straight line from the side-wall, creating two parallel side-walls which narrow towards the extension's edge. Then from 1/3 from the tip of the free edge view, "cut" and narrow at a 45° angle creating with a slightly rounded tip.

- The three lines: lower arch, upper arch and finger's axis are parallel.

- The apex placement: 1/3 or between 1/3 – 2/3 away from the cuticle.

- Standard nail – product is easily balanced over the entire nail.

- Hooked nail – the majority of product is in the middle of the nail, on the top of the natural free edge, at its deepest point. Small amount of product is applied on the top of the natural nail apex, which is already very high.

- Nail biter – the majority of the product is on the nail plate over the apex, to balance the nail and create straight application from the apex to the extension's edge.

Filing technique

The 10-step Filing technique applies here as well. You'll file the nail exactly the same way as the square nail. The only difference here is that you'll have to file the tip of the extension in a 45° angle and follow the narrowing shape of the side walls.

Merilyn shape

This is an over pinched square nail shape. It creates a very deep C-curve and narrows to the tip. The longer the nail, the more difference you will see. The wide nails are tricky to do, as no matter how much you pinch, the shape looks pretty much like a square and tapers gently towards the extension's edge from the apex.

Standard nail - Gel natural look technique

Standard nail
top view

Standard nail
side view

Standard nail
front view

Hooked nail - Acrylic P&W (in color) with nail bed elongation

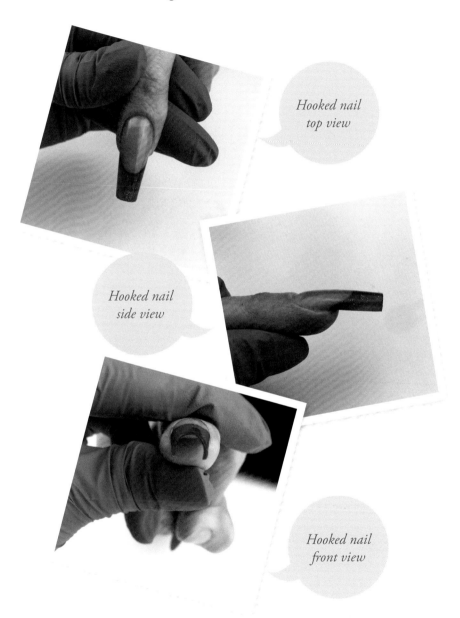

Hooked nail
top view

Hooked nail
side view

Hooked nail
front view

Bitten nail - Acrylic natural look technique

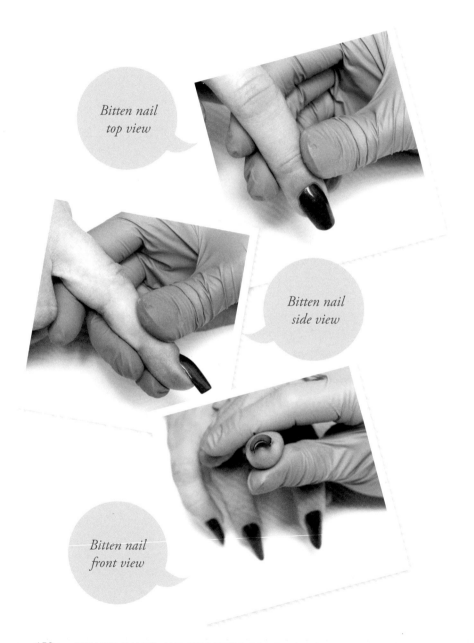

Bitten nail
top view

Bitten nail
side view

Bitten nail
front view

Form application

The form is applied straight to the finger and to the nail, so it doesn't go up or drop down. The standard and bitten nail form is applied like this. When on the hooked nail the form must be slightly lifted to about the height of the apex, but no higher.

Standard nail side view

Hooked nail side view

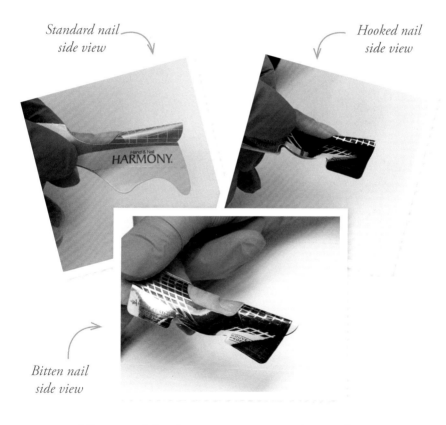

Bitten nail side view

The tip of the form stays open and round.

Standard nail front view

Hooked nail front view

Bitten nail front view

The form creates the straight elongation of the middle line of the finger and fits nicely around the free edge.

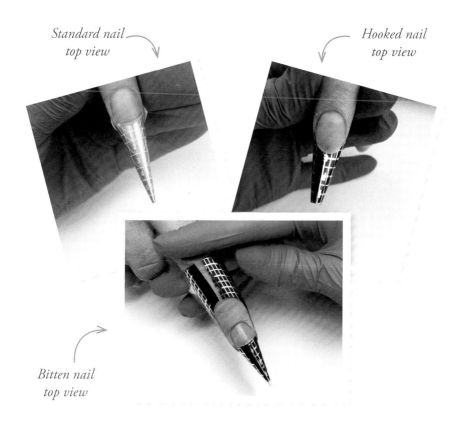

Standard nail top view

Hooked nail top view

Bitten nail top view

The form checklist's points must be ticked.

Product application

Follow the same procedure as for the square shape. The only difference here is that the apex is slightly moved forward towards the natural free edge, and placed about 2/3 away from the cuticle area. From that point, gently tapers towards the extension's edge.

Filing technique

Use the 10-step Filing technique and shape the same way you would a square nail.

Gothic Almond

The Gothic Almond is a mix of the Stiletto shape and the Russian Almond. The side view looks similar to the Russian Almond, but is pinched to be narrower. The upper arch runs in a Stiletto shape.

Standard nail - Gel natural look technique

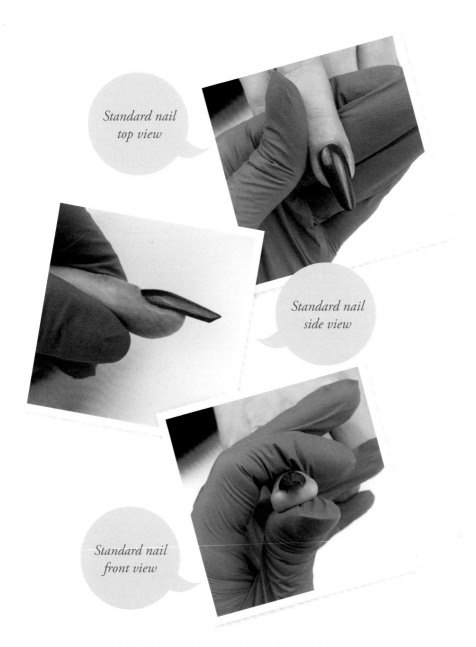

Standard nail
top view

Standard nail
side view

Standard nail
front view

Hooked nail - Acrylic P&W (in color) with nail bed elongation

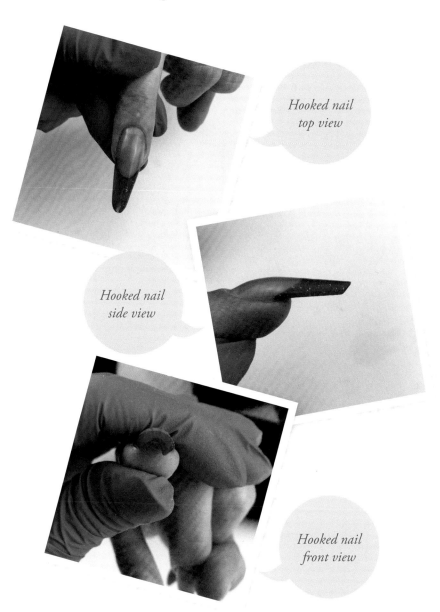

Hooked nail top view

Hooked nail side view

Hooked nail front view

Bitten nail - Acrylic natural look technique

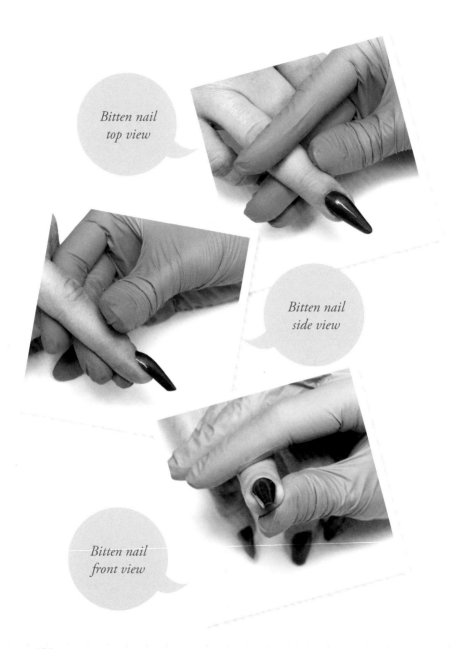

Bitten nail
top view

Bitten nail
side view

Bitten nail
front view

Form application

The general rule says the form should be applied straight, so the upper arch is parallel to the side wall. That is the truth when the nail is being done on a standard and hooked nail. When it comes to a bitten nail, that rule doesn't always apply. If the nail is very high at the free edge, then apply the form like for the stiletto shape – downwards. That will allow you to achieve better structure and will be easier to apply the product in the correct way.

Standard nail side view

Hooked nail side view

Bitten nail side view

The form closes into a stiletto shape when viewed from the top. The tip is completely closed.

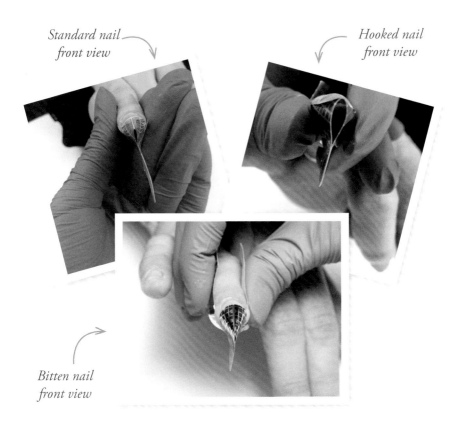

Standard nail front view

Hooked nail front view

Bitten nail front view

Make sure the form is straight and ticks all the general rules.

Standard nail top view

Hooked nail top view

Bitten nail top view

Product application

- The side walls are parallel and narrow to the tip.

- The free edge creates a stiletto shape, but the tip is tilted at 45° angle.

- The apex is between 1/3 – 2/3 away from the cuticle area.

- Make sure the product is applied low enough to create straight lower arch.

Filing technique

The 10-step Filing technique applies.

<u>The differences here are</u>:

- The tip of the free edge is angled at 45° and is gently rounded.

- The nail tapers from the apex downwards to the extension's edge, so file according to that angle.

Edge shape

This is one of the most demanding shapes, especially when creating P&W with the nail bed elongation (the elongated nail bed ends in a "V" shape, as the extension's edge). The reason this is so demanding is because if the form has been applied squint, or the tip of the nail bed and extension don't match, it will be a little disaster. Having said that, I still like that shape, that's why I've included it in this book.

Standard nail - Gel natural look technique

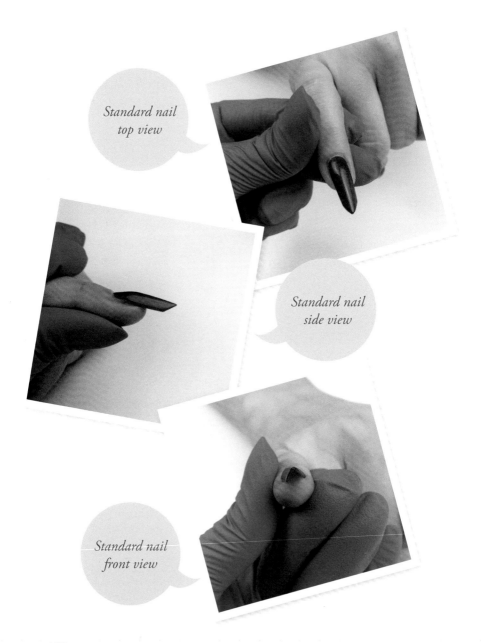

Standard nail
top view

Standard nail
side view

Standard nail
front view

Hooked nail - Acrylic P&W (in color) with nail bed elongation

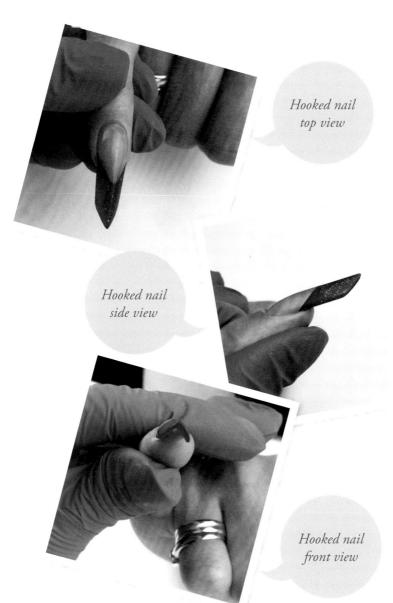

Hooked nail
top view

Hooked nail
side view

Hooked nail
front view

Bitten nail - Acrylic natural look technique

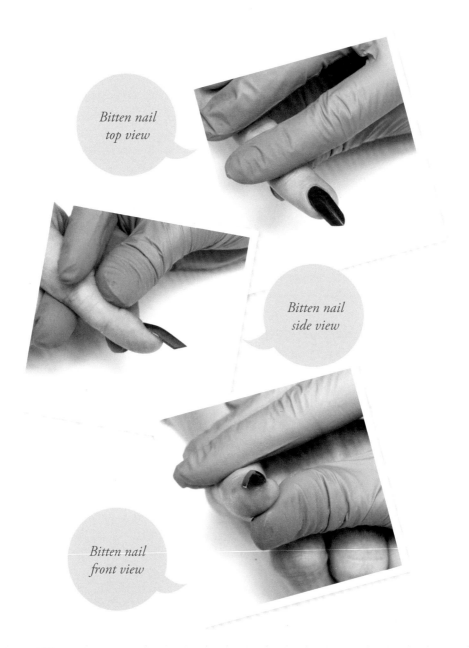

Bitten nail
top view

Bitten nail
side view

Bitten nail
front view

Form application

The form is applied straight to the finger and as high as the apex. Before you apply the form onto a hooked nail make sure the free edge has been completely filed off, as that will ensure correct form placement.

For the edge shape, apart from the two slits on both sides of the smile line (the general principles of customizing the form), make a tiny cut in the central line from the free edge area. This cut is crucial to correct form application.

Standard nail side view

Hooked nail side view

Bitten nail side view.

The tip of the form closes in a diamond shape, so the concave will create a "roof" extension and the convex will have the edge.

Standard nail front view

Hooked nail front view

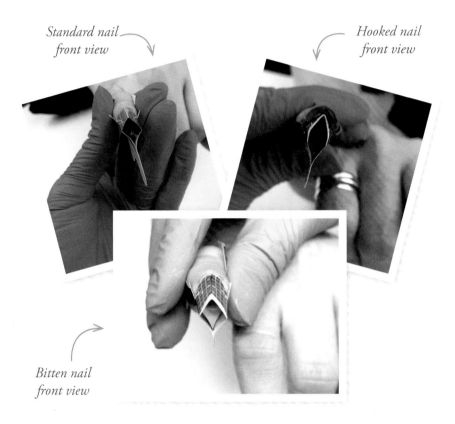

Bitten nail front view

The form is straight to the finger and perfectly fit under the free edge and around the fingertip.

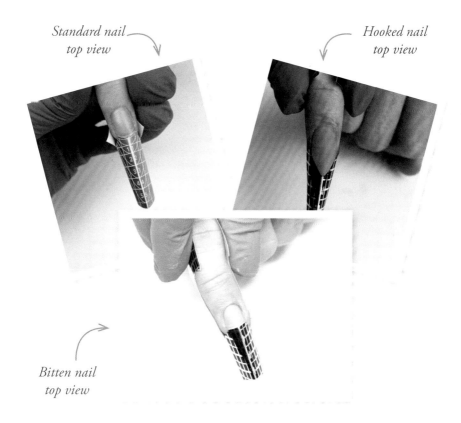

Standard nail top view

Hooked nail top view

Bitten nail top view

Product application

- The extension's edge creates a "roof," so make sure you apply the product evenly on both sides of the form.

- Start by creating the length in the edge of the form, then take it downwards to both sides and the corners of the smile line.

- The tip ends in a sharp point.

- The side walls are parallel and run in a straight line from the smile line corners.

- The end of the side wall is tilted at a 45° angle.

- Apply extra product on the edge to define it.

Filing technique

Yes, the 10-step Filing technique applies here as well, but some major differences are in steps 1 and 2.

The differences are:

- File the free edge from the lower arch upwards to the central edge. Make sure the file is flat and parallel to that side. Repeat on the second side.

- Next, place the file flat on a side wall. This time the file is straight to the finger. The edge is being filed too. Keep filing up and down to establish the sharp edge. Repeat on the other side.

- Very gently smooth the edge.

- Shape the end of the extension to a 45° angle, finishing with a pointy tip.

- Follow the rest of the steps of the Filing technique.

There you have it – eight different shapes, but as you can see they are done in a very similar way. The most important thing here is to know how to structure the nail and apply the form. Once you know it, then you're able to create any shape you like.

NOTES:

THE NAIL SHAPES AND STRUCTURE COMPENDIUM

Next Step

—wu—

Now, knowing everything about creating the correct nail structure and general rules for any shape, you should put it into practice. That's the only way to get better. Yes it's that simple, but may be tricky at first. If you cannot practice right away, don't worry, that's the beauty of any written and recorded material; you can go back to it over and over again, whenever you need to. Use this book as your guide and reach for it as often as you like.

In my experience with reading, I know that sometimes you may not get a clear vision of the "how to," you're looking for. Reading is a great start in getting clarity about all the shapes and structures, but if you're anything like me, a visual person, then following a step by step training is what you should do next to get better and faster results.

While taking photos for this book I was also recording everything at the same time. I then created an on-line training course for people like you, who would like to dig deeper and learn by watching, not only reading.

In that training course I explain the general rules using my flipchart first, by drawing shapes and diagrams, so you will fully understand everything. Then I teach a nail prep using an electric drill, form customization and placement, product application, pinching techniques; depending on the shape and product used, and finally my 10-step Filing technique. You'll see me creating all eight shapes described in this book on 3 different nail types: standard, hooked and bitten. That also covers acrylic and gel systems using my top techniques. So, you'll benefit from this training whether you're working with gel or acrylic.

Having a book, which you can keep in the salon and reach for whenever needed need it, plus a training course where you can study each move and fully understand how to do everything covered in this book—that's a MUST HAVE full package if you're serious about cracking this subject (www.elaloszczyk.co.uk).

Recommended Resources

You'll find all my training courses and books at www.elaloszczyk.co.uk, so you can learn from me no matter where you are.

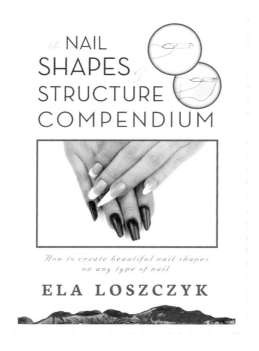

The Nail Shapes and Structure Masterclass on-line training course

The most comprehensive on-line training course that teaches you various nail shapes and structures on any nail type.

Paint like a PRO - One Stroke Foundation DVD training course

If you ever wanted to create beautiful designs using acrylic paints, but don't consider yourself an artist, then this training is going to become your "bible."

I'll teach you here how to create any design, by explaining to you and braking down various one stroke moves, so you won't struggle anymore. Once you know the moves, you'll be able to create or re-create any design.

You'll also learn in detail:

- about the paints and colour blending;

- brushes and how to use them;

- various moves to create stunning designs;

- 3 designs you can use straight away;

- 5 bonus designs to re-create.

"I want to assure you that anyone can create beautiful nail art, as it's all about technique."

One Stroke Designs Vol. I DVD training course

10 fantastic One Stroke Designs combined with acrylic and gel, transfer foil, crystals, etc. I'll explain each design on a flip chart first, so you'll get an idea of how to plan any design. I'll then guide you step-by-step about transferring that design to a tip. Easy to follow instructions with no steps missed! You'll love it and your clients will love you even more!

3D Acrylic Design Foundation DVD training course

3D Acrylic Design Foundation DVD training is a perfect solution for those of you

- who feel that plain salon nails are not enough,

- who want to express themselves in different way,

- who want to learn a new skill or improve existing one

You will learn my secrets of:

- perfect blending and fading,

- various patterns,

- 3 award winning techniques of different type of petals/ leaves creating, which helped me win competitions,

- encapsulation,

- designs which can be used on daily basis and also special occasions such as wedding, party or holidays (flowers, fruits, mushroom, butterflies and more!)

YOU WILL LOVE this DVD training!

I've structured and created this training with YOU in my mind and to make it as simple

as possible for you to learn.

In this class I:

- brake everything into easy to follow step by steps,

- explain those steps as I go so you can really understand what and why

PLUS

- share my little secrets which I've learned over all those years from other top techs.

Win the Nail Game - Competition success made simple

This book has been written to inspire you to do more, reach your goals, to enter nail competitions, and to push your boundaries and never stop learning.

I divided this book into three parts to really dive into every aspect, giving you as much information as possible.

Part I Getting ready for the competitions will teach you how to prepare yourself, what is important, and what steps and actions must be taken if you want to do well on the big day.

Part II Competition day tells you what to do and what not to do on that day. You'll also find here, done for you, product checklist and other important aspects to be implemented for you and your model.

Part III After the competition, it is all about getting feedback, learning from your experience, and making the most out of it for your business.